PUBLICATION No. 9
of the Mathematics Research Center
United States Army
The University of Wisconsin

STATISTICAL THEORY OF RELIABILITY

STATISTICAL THEORY OF RELIABILITY

Proceedings of an Advanced Seminar Conducted by the Mathematics Research Center, United States Army, at the University of Wisconsin, Madison, May 8-10, 1962

edited by
MARVIN ZELEN

MADISON · THE UNIVERSITY OF WISCONSIN PRESS · 1963

Published by
THE UNIVERSITY OF WISCONSIN PRESS
430 Sterling Court, Madison 6, Wisconsin

Prepared for the camera by Phyllis J. Kern
Printed in the United States of America by
North Central Publishing Company, Inc. St. Paul, Minnesota

Library of Congress Catalog Card Number 63-9061

AUTHORS

Richard E. Barlow,
    General Telephone and Electronics Laboratories, Inc.

Larry C. Hunter,
    General Telephone and Electronics Laboratories, Inc.

Frank Proschan,
    Boeing Scientific Research Laboratories

Joan Raup Rosenblatt,
    National Bureau of Standards

George H. Weiss
    University of Maryland and National Bureau of Standards

William W. Wolman,
    National Aeronautics and Space Agency

PARTICIPANTS

Banzhaf, Robert, Ordnance Ammunition Command, U.S. Army
Barlow, Richard E., General Telephone and Electronics Laboratories
Box, George E. P., University of Wisconsin
Bulfinch, Alonzo, Picatinny Arsenal, U.S. Army
Collins, Elmer F., U.S. Navy Bureau of Weapons
Connor, William S., Research Triangle Institute
Corcoran, W. J., U.S. Navy Special Projects Office
Coy, John W., White Sands Missile Range
Draper, N., University of Wisconsin
Ellner, Henry, U.S. Army Chemical Corps
Esary, James D., Boeing Research Laboratories
Flehinger, Betty J., International Business Machines
Frishman, Fred, Army Research Office
Gorenstein, Samuel, System Development Corp.
Grubbs, Frank E., Aberdeen Proving Ground
Gurland, John, Mathematics Research Center, U.S. Army
Harter, H. Leon, Aeronautical Research Laboratories, Wright-
    Patterson AFB
Hixson, Eugene E., NASA, Goddard Space Flight Center
Hunter, Larry C., General Telephone and Electronics Laboratories
Itoh, Makoto, Mathematics Research Center, U.S. Army
Kao, John H. K., Bell Telephone Laboratories, and Cornell University
Keller, Joseph B., Institute of Mathematical Sciences, New York
    University
Krimmer, Manfred W., Picatinny Arsenal, U.S. Army
Kurkjian, Badrig, Diamond Ordnance Fuze Laboratories, U.S. Army
Lehman, Alfred, Mathematics Research Center, U.S. Army
Levenbach, G.L., Bell Telephone Laboratories
Maloney, Clifford J., U.S. Army Chemical Corps Biological Labs.
Mantel, Nathan, National Cancer Institute
Moy, W., University of Wisconsin
Okano, Fred, National Aeronautics and Space Administration

Parrish, Gene B., Army Research Office (Durham)
Proschan, Frank, Boeing Research Laboratories
Rajaramen, V., University of Wisconsin
Reinhardt, Howard, Mathematics Research Center, U.S. Army, and
    Montana State University
Rosenblatt, Joan R., National Bureau of Standards
Rotkin, Israel, Diamond Ordnance Fuze Laboratories, U.S. Army
Seidman, Thomas, Mathematics Research Center, U. S. Army
Seth, B. R., Mathematics Research Center, U.S. Army, and the Indian
    Institute of Technology, Kharagpur
Shaw, Oliver A., AFOSR
Shratter, Benjamin, NASA, Marshall Space Flight Center
Spears, Otis S., U.S. Army Artillery and Missile School, Ft. Sill
Steck, G. P., Sandia Corporation
Strong, T. M., International Business Machines
Walker, James W., Georgia Institute of Technology
Weinstein, Joseph, U.S. Army Signal Research and Development
    Laboratory
Weiss, George, University of Maryland, and National Bureau of
    Standards
Wiggins, Alvin D., Hanford Laboratories
Wolman, William, NASA, Goddard Space Flight Center
Yuan, H.C., University of Wisconsin
Zelen, Marvin, Mathematics Research Center, U.S. Army
Zenkere, Kenneth M., Reconnaissance Systems, Sylvania Corp.
Zitron, Norman, Mathematics Research Center, U.S. Army

FOREWORD

This conference was the first venture by the Mathematics Research Center, U.S. Army, to sponsor a meeting, which in outlook, was similar in spirit to a seminar, rather than a symposium. Hence this conference was called an "advanced seminar." The plan consisted of inviting six recognized authorities currently working in the statistical theory of reliability. They were asked to prepare papers which were mainly expository in content. The aim was to survey current important work and bring the seminar participants up to the frontiers of recent research. Each session was devoted to a single topic. In addition to the main speaker, an invited discussant elaborated on the main presentation. In order to encourage discussion, the number of seminar participants was limited. Attendance was by invitation only. Invitations were extended to statisticians, mathematicians, and scientists having interest in the Statistical Theory of Reliability.

The seminar was opened by a short welcome address by Professor Rudolph E. Langer, Director of the Mathematics Research Center, U.S. Army. Opening remarks were made by Professor Marvin Zelen, Conference Chairman. The sessions were presided over by invited chairmen. These were:

Professor George E. P. Box, University of Wisconsin
Professor Norman Draper, University of Wisconsin
Dr. Frank Grubbs, Ballistic Research Laboratories, Aberdeen
    Proving Grounds
Professor John Gurland, Mathematics Research Center, U. S. Army
Professor V. Rajarman, University of Wisconsin
Professor Howard Reinhardt, Mathematics Research Center,
    U.S. Army, and Montana State University

The invited discussants were:

Dr. R. E. Barlow, General Telephone and Electronics Laboratories,
    Inc.
Dr. W.S. Connor, Research Triangle Institute

Dr. James D. Esary, Boeing Scientific Research Laboratories
Dr. Betty J. Flehinger, Thomas J. Watson Research Center,
   IBM Corporation
Dr. George Steck, Sandia Corporation
Prof. George H. Weiss, National Bureau of Standards and
   University of Maryland

A dinner was held on the evening of May 8. The principal speaker
at the dinner was Professor James F. Crow, Department of Medical
Genetics, University of Wisconsin.

The papers are arranged in the order in which they were presented
with the exception of the paper by Weiss which is given first because
of its extensive nature. Sincere thanks go to the speakers, chairman,
invited discussants, and especially to the attendees, who all contributed to making this advanced seminar a stimulating and lively
affair.

PREFACE

Technology has been characterized in the past decade by the development of complex systems containing large numbers of subsystems, components, and parts. The trend to ever larger and more complex systems is continuing with the development of space vehicles, electronic computers, communication systems, weapons systems, etc. The children's nursery rhyme, "For want of a nail, the kingdom was lost," applies to complex systems. The failure of a single inexpensive part or component may cause the failure of the entire system. In the past, a system was developed with the purpose of "making it work." Such luxuries can no longer be afforded with complex systems. Today, complex systems must be developed to not only work, but to work reliably. Reliability is the concern of all scientists and engineers engaged in developing a system, from the design, through the manufacturing, to its ultimate use. If the system is not designed to be reliable, no amount of careful manufacturing will improve the systems reliability. On the other hand, systems designed with high reliability may perform poorly due to absence of good quality control in the building of the system. Again, poor maintenance will obviate the benefits of superior design and production. Highly reliable systems are not accidents or coincidences, but the result of conscious effort by all concerned.

High reliability goals needed by systems designers may at times appear hopeless and unobtainable. Yet the examples set by the reliability of biological systems serve as proof that high reliability of systems can be obtained, even by use of unreliable components. Loss of major subsystems does not necessarily cause complete failure of biological systems. Biological systems have built-in redundant elements and are capable of self-repair. The principles by which biological systems function with near perfect reliability are not well understood and are under active investigation. These same ideas, borrowed from biological systems, are being used to improve the reliability of man-made complex systems.

Statisticians have responded to the needs of engineers and scientists by developing new statistical techniques and methods particularly suitable for use in reliability applications. In the past, a great many of the advances in the theories of probability and statistics have been initially motivated by real problems. Investigators have been quick to gain new insights, develop needed techniques, and pose subtle theoretical problems when confronted with novel problem settings. The first step in the application of mathematics to a physical problem is the construction of a mathematical model which embodies the main observational and theoretical features of the phenomenon. When the phenomenon is dependent on chance mechanisms, the mathematical model will be probabilistic in character. Many of the topics in this volume are concerned with model building as statisticians are still in the initial stages of developing a statistical theory of reliability. With the exception of life testing techniques, the statistical problems of estimation, inference, verification, prediction, and decision-making have had only a rudimentary beginning.

This volume not only contains a summary of the major statistical and probabilistic results associated with the theory of reliability, but also cites problem areas; with few exceptions most work on these problems has only started within the past decade. Hence few of the major results have found their way into recent books on probability and statistics. One of the purposes of publishing these papers is to help overcome the lag between the discovery of important results and their implementation in applications. Also this volume is a record of current progress and may be used as a source for research problems. It is hoped that these papers can serve as a basis for seminars, informal talks, and as supplementary material for engineers, mathematicians, statisticians, and other scientists concerned with reliability.

Marvin Zelen
November 1962

CONTENTS

PROBLEMS IN SYSTEM RELIABILITY ANALYSIS,
William Wolman

STATISTICAL THEORY OF RELIABILITY

GEORGE H. WEISS

A survey of some mathematical models in the theory of reliability

I. Introduction

While quality control has always been of some concern in manufacturing ventures, it is only during the period from the second world
war to the present that reliability has become of major concern to all
parts of the engineering community. At the present time it is realized
that complex modern designs carry within them the possibility of many
types of error and malfunction. Therefore, it is the job of the design
engineer not only to assure a possibility of proper functioning but also
to take into account the failure properties of the system to be designed.
While such reliability considerations can seem staggering, and specified reliability goals seem unattainable to the designer of military
systems, the tantalizing example set by the reliability of biological
systems is proof that extremely high reliabilities can be achieved by
combinations of unreliable elements. The principles behind the
achievement of such near perfection are only partly understood and
are presently under active investigation. It is the purpose of this
article to review some of the major ideas and results in the modern
theory of reliability. We will discuss only the model aspects of reliability without entering into the equally important questions of how
one tests the validity of a given model or the estimation of model
parameters. An excellent bibliography on life testing and related
topics is to be found in [M7].

Roughly speaking we shall discuss three aspects of reliability.
The first which we call the topological aspect is concerned with the
relation between the reliability of individual components and the reliability of the system as a whole. In such a case the system reliability will be considered as a function of the interconnection of
components, or of the topology of the network. The second aspect to
be discussed is the time dependence of reliability, i.e., we will be
concerned with the statistics of such matters as the mean time between
failures, the number of failures in a given time, and so on. Finally,

we shall discuss several models relating to the economics of equipment maintenance. Here we will consider the simplest possible models for the effects of periodic or other types of equipment replacement or surveillance. Many models with particular applications have been discussed in the literature of management science. We will discuss only the simplest possible results which have been analyzed in the context of the maintenance of reliability.

The categorization that we have just introduced is not meant to imply that a specific practical problem can be pigeonholed into a single classification. Most frequently a situation will require all three types of analyses. There are, however, some occasions when one of the categories given in the last paragraph will exactly fit the situation. For example when designing a fuzing system for a weapon, one requires the components to operate only once when actuated; hence the time dependent reliability of these components is of no interest unless the system is held in storage long enough for aging effects to be important. On the other hand, if one designs a radio communications network, the time-dependent failure characteristics of the components are of direct interest, and also the optimal preventive maintenance policy with respect to a given cost criterion. Both of these will obviously depend on the topology of the network.

As are most survey articles, this one is written in accordance with the author's personal interests and prejudices. For this reason the most complete coverage is given to topics in renewal theory and the theory of machine maintenance; the theory of the topological aspects of reliability is less adequately discussed. Furthermore I have tried to describe general results rather than analyses of particular systems.

Most of the works referred to in the present paper have appeared in Western journals. There is a good deal of Russian literature on reliability but it does not reflect the careful mathematical analysis that characterizes Russian contributions in the field of control systems, and we have not bothered to summarize it. A forthcoming paper by J. R. Rosenblatt and D. D. Prill will contain abstracts of about 100 Russian papers on reliability.

II. Topological Reliability

In this section we will discuss the simplest models for reliability considered as a function of system connectivity. The description of systems is quite general, but the analysis of reliability will be developed only for the case of statistically independent components.

To introduce this subject we shall use the concept of reliability diagram, as shown in Figure 1. At the outset we assume that the network may be characterized as a black box with I input terminals and 0 output terminals. Internal to the box are a number of elements which form connected paths between the input and

and output terminals. We may or may not allow an element such as C to function as part of two paths, even though it may be eligible to function in both paths. In the system shown element C functions as part of only a single path. It is assumed that some of the elements may be inoperative due to component failures. The major problems in topological reliability can be stated in terms of this model as follows: It is required to transfer information from a given subset of input terminals to a subset of the output terminals. The subset of output terminals may or may not be given (as an example, it may be required to transfer information from a given input terminal to any output terminal). Given the reliability characteristics of the individual elements and a description of the interconnections, it is required to find the reliability of the system, i.e., the probability that the system will convey the information according to the design. In this section we discuss only single shot probabilities, i.e., we shall comput the reliability assuming that the system is to function only once.

A tacit assumption in the preceding problem statement is that each element is capable of being in only one of two states, and that system performance can be called either "successful" or "failure." In many instances intermediate states of elements and of the system as a whole, are possible. The extension of the present analysis to a situation involving n (> 2) possible states is not difficult in principle, but the question of defining the state of the system in terms of the individual element states must be examined for every particular case. We will therefore restrict the present discussion to the two state situation since it has a wide range of applicability.

Let us therefore label the paths connecting input terminal j to output terminal k by $P_{jk}(n)$, where $n = 1, 2, \ldots, N_{jk}$ and N_{jk} is the total number of paths linking j to k . We define the function

$$R\left(P_{jk}(n_1) \cdot P_{jk}(n_2) \cdots P_{jk}(n_m)\right)$$

to be the probability that paths $n_1, n_2, \ldots, n_m$ between points j and k are simultaneously operable. We further define an array of functions $S_{jk}(m)$ by

$$S_{jk}(m) = \sum_{n_1} \sum_{n_2} \cdots \sum_{n_m} R\left(P_{jk}(n_1) \cdot P_{jk}(n_2) \cdots P_{jk}(n_m)\right) \qquad (2.1)$$

$$N_{jk} \geq n_1 > n_2 > \cdots > n_m \geq 1.$$

Then, an application of tne inclusion-exclusion theorem for probabilities, [F2, W1], yields for the probability that at least one path will be operable between terminals j and k ,

$$R_{jk}(1) = S_{jk}(1) - S_{jk}(2) + S_{jk}(3) - \ldots \qquad (2.2)$$

The probability that exactly r out of the totality of N_{jk} paths be operable is

$$P_{jk}(r, N_{jk}) = S_{jk}(r) - \binom{r+1}{r} S_{jk}(r+1) + \binom{r+2}{r} S_{jk}(r+2)$$

$$- \ldots + (-1)^{N_{jk}-r} \binom{N_{jk}}{r} S_{jk}(N_{jk}) \, . \qquad (2.3)$$

The probability that at least r out of N_{jk} paths be operable is

$$R_{jk}(r, N_{jk}) = S_{jk}(r) - \binom{r}{r-1} S_{jk}(r+1) + \binom{r+1}{r-1} S_{jk}(r+2)$$

$$- \ldots + (-1)^{N_{jk}-r} S_{jk}(N_{jk}) \, . \qquad (2.4)$$

The formulae, Eqs. (2-1)-(2.4) furnish us with the possibility of defining reliability in several different ways. For example, we may
define reliability to be the probability that a single path be operable
between an input terminal and a set, C, of output terminals. Then
we need only define

$$S_{jC}(m) = \sum_{n_1} \sum_{n_2} \cdots \sum_{n_m} R\Big(P_{jk_1}(n_1) \cdot P_{jk_1}(n_2) \cdots P_{jk_2}(n_r) \cdot P_{jk_2}(n_{r+1}) \cdots P_{jk_s}(n_t) \cdot P_{jk_s}(n_{t+1}) \cdots P_{jk_s}(n_m)\Big)$$

$$N_{jC} \geq n_1 > n_2 > \cdots > n_m > 1$$

$$(2.5)$$

for $C = \{k_1, k_2, \ldots k_s\}$ where N_{jC} is the total number of paths
linking point j to some point in C and use the obvious analog of
Eq.(2.2) to find the reliability. Other more complicated generalizations readily suggest themselves.

The reader will observe that we have not yet completed the solution of the problem posed in the first paragraph of this section. The
completion was deferred so that it would be clear at this point that no
assumption about independence of components has been made, and
indeed none is necessary provided that we may have some way of
calculating the fundamental quantities $S_{jk}(m)$. Further details of the
model are needed in order to relate component reliabilities to the
path probabilities which enter into the calculation of Eq. (2.2). The
most common assumption is that component failures occur independentl
If we assume that a given path P is composed of N elements in

series, of which the jth element has reliability R_j , and that the state of any element is independent of the state of the remaining elements, we can immediately write

$$S_{1n}(1) = \prod_{j=1}^{N} R_j .$$

(2.6)

The reliability of a path which contains N components in parallel is defined by

$$S_{12}(1) = 1 - \prod_{j=1}^{N} (1-R_j) .$$

(2.7)

Similar results were obtained by Gates, [G1] and Broussard, [B18].

The usual mode for a series network contains a single input and a single output terminal. A recent investigation of the reliability of computers which operate in parallel, has required the study of a model which might be called a generalization of the series network, [W6]. In this type of network, pictured in Fig. 2 we consider several input and output terminals.

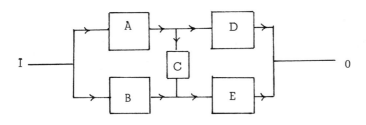

Figure 1.   Reliability diagram.

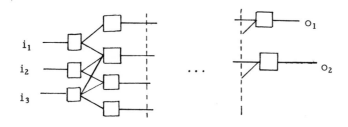

Figure 2.   Generalized series network.

The salient feature of this network is the fact that it can be considered to operate in successive stages. The operability of at least a single component from each stage as well as at least one sensing and switching mechanism between successive stages being required for the successful operation of the entire system. If we introduce a column vector $\underline{R}(n) = (r_j(n))$ such that $r_j(n)$ is the probability that the element of information introduced at the first stage is now at component j in the nth stage, and a transition matrix $\underline{M}(n) = (m_{ij}(n))$ where $m_{ij}(n)$ is the probability that an element of information at component i at stage $n-1$ can be successfully transferred to component j at stage n, we can write

$$\underline{R}(n) = \underline{M}(n)\,\underline{M}(n-1)\cdots\underline{M}(1)\,R(0) \tag{2.8}$$

where $\underline{R}(0)$ contains the input data. The failure state must be taken into account in the description of the system.

The reference given above prescribes rules for the calculation of the matrix elements of $\underline{M}(n)$ in terms of the switching rules. Both determinate and random switching between stages are taken into account. Many definitions of reliability are possible in this general scheme but they all involve the calculation of one or all of the elements of $\underline{R}(N)$, the final state vector for the system.

The general question of the characterization of the topological properties of networks for the purpose of discussing reliability has been examined by Birnbaum, Esary, and Saunders, [B11]. They begin by specifying the state of an n component system to be a vector $\underline{x} = (x_1, x_2, \ldots, x_n)$ where $x_i = 1$ means "i^{th} component performs" and $x_i = 0$ means "i^{th} component fails." They then define the state of the network by means of a structure function $\Phi(\underline{x})$ which can be either 0 or 1 and which tells whether the network as a whole does or does not perform. A path, as we have used the term in the preceding discussion is any vector $\underline{x}$ for which $\Phi(\underline{x}) = 1$. The structure function for a network with n components in parallel is written as

$$\Phi(\underline{x}) = 1 - \prod_{i=1}^{n}(1-x_i) = \max(x_1, x_2, \ldots, x_n) \tag{2.9}$$

and that for n components in series is

$$\Phi(\underline{x}) = \prod_{i=1}^{n} x_i = \min(x_1, x_2, \ldots, x_n) \tag{2.10}$$

The structure function for the network of Fig. 1 is given by an expression of the form of Eq. (2.11)

$$\Phi(x) = x_A x_D + x_B x_E + x_A x_C x_E - x_A x_C x_D x_E - x_A x_D x_B x_E - x_A x_B x_C x_E$$
$$+ x_A x_B x_C x_D x_E . \tag{2.11}$$

The three authors then proceed to define the composition of lower
order structures into larger structures. The order of a structure is the
number n of components. That is to say, they define a structure of
order n+1 to be a combination of structures $\lambda(\underline{x})$ and $\mu(\underline{x})$ of order
n when the following identity holds:

$$\Phi(x_1, x_2, \ldots, x_n, x_{n+1}) = x_{n+1}\lambda(\underline{x}) + (1-x_{n+1})\mu(\underline{x}) \ . \qquad (2.12)$$

Any structure of order n+1 can be represented in this form by means
of the identity

$$\Phi(x_1, x_2, \ldots, x_{n+1}) = x_{n+1}\Phi(x_1, x_2, \ldots, x_n, 1) + (1-x_{n+1})\Phi(x_1, x_2, \ldots, x_n, 0)$$

$$(2.13)$$

which implies that the decomposition can be ultimately carried out in
terms of order one.

Further information on the structure of networks can be obtained
by using the notions of coherent and semi-coherent structures. A
structure is said to be semi-coherent if

$$\Phi(\underline{y}) \geq \Phi(\underline{x}) \quad \text{for all} \quad \underline{y} \geq \underline{x} \qquad (2.14)$$

where the relation $\underline{y} \geq \underline{x}$ is defined by $y_1 \geq x_1$, $y_2 \geq x_2, \ldots$.
A structure is said to be coherent if it is semi-coherent and

$$\Phi(\underline{0}) = 0 \ , \quad \Phi(\underline{1}) = 1 \ . \qquad (2.15)$$

Thus, most physically reasonable circuits are coherent, since the
definition simply says that the system will not operate when no element is operating and it will operate when all of the elements are
operating. Birnbaum, Esary, and Saunders prove the following theorem
on structure functions:

> A structure $\Phi(x_1, x_2, \ldots, x_{n+1})$ is semi-coherent if and
> only if it can be represented as a linear combination of
> functions of order n in the form of Eq.(2.12) with
> $\lambda(\underline{x})$ and $\mu(\underline{x})$ (a) semi-coherent, and (b) such that
> $\lambda(\underline{x}) \geq \mu(\underline{x})$ for all $\underline{x}$. It is coherent if and only if
> in addition to(a) and(b) either (c_1) $\lambda(\underline{x}) = \mu(\underline{x})$ for
> all $\underline{x}$ and $\lambda(\underline{x})$ is coherent; or (c_2) $\lambda(\underline{x}) > \mu(\underline{x})$ for
> some $\underline{x}$.

Starting from this theorem the authors show how to construct the class
of all coherent structures. Further results are then given on the
characterization of paths which are irreducible. A reducible path is
one in which the presence or absence of a single component or group
of components has no effect on the structure function. An irreducible

path is one that is not reducible. An enumerative scheme for reducing
a network to its irreducible form is then given. Most of the work on
structure theorems is closely related to similar problems for switching
networks. Moskowitz and collaborators, [M6], have published a
number of papers on structure theorems, using boolean algebra methods
which are extensively used in the design of switching circuits. Many
results pertaining to the characterization of the reliability properties
of networks can be couched in graph-theoretic terms, [W11]. No
generalizations of this type of work have been given in the literature
for systems in which the elements x_i can be in more than two states.
This is true, in part, to the lack of any method of sufficient generality,
for defining the value of $\Phi(\underline{x})$ given the value of $\underline{x}$.

The value of the state of any element x_i is a random variable,
and the reliability of the element is just the expectation of x_i,

$$R_i = E(x_i) \ . \tag{2.16}$$

The question of primary importance in reliability analyses can therefore be posed as the problem of finding the expectation of $\Phi(\underline{x})$,

$$R = E[\Phi(\underline{x})] \tag{2.17}$$

where R is the reliability of the system. If the element states $\{x_i\}$
are independent random variables then any term x_i^n should be replaced
by x_i since x_i is idempotent. Hence we have the result

$$R = E[\Phi(x_1, x_2, \ldots, x_n)] = \Phi(E(x_1), E(x_2), \ldots, E(x_n)) = \Phi(R_1, R_2, \ldots, R_n) \tag{2.18}$$

where we have assumed that $\Phi(x_1, x_2, \ldots, x_n)$ has been reduced to
a form in which x_j appears to a power no higher than the first. This,
however, is valid only for independent elements. With this restriction
we also have, using Eq. (2.13),

$$\frac{\partial R}{\partial R_i} = \Phi(\underline{R})\big|_{R_i=1} - \Phi(\underline{R})\big|_{R_i=0} \tag{2.19}$$

where $\underline{R} = (R_1, R_2, \ldots R_n)$, since the variable x_{n+1} in Eq. (2.13)
can obviously be interchanged with any of the state variables.

A special case of the preceding formulae that has been extensively
studied is that of a system for which $R_1 = R_2 = \ldots = R_n = \rho$, that is,
a network with independent elements each of which has the same
failure properties. This work was stimulated by a paper by von Neumann [N2], which discussed the possibility of attaining reliabilities
by mechanical means of the same order of magnitude as those in the
nervous system. The crux of the problem is that a neuron, or a relay,
to put it into mechanical terms, is capable of introducing two types of

malfunctioning into a system. The first type is a relay closure when none is called for, and the second type is a non closure when the relay is actuated. When the elements of a network introduce only a single type of error, the network can be designed to be arbitrarily reliable by simply combining enough elements in parallel. However, it is general- ly the case that when the elements with two types of error are combined in parallel one set of errors will be diminished by the redundancy while the second set of errors will be enhanced. As a simple example of this consider a single relay with probability p of closing if actuated and probability ε of closing before any actuation. If n elements are connected in parallel, the reliability of the system for a single actuation is

$$R = (1-\varepsilon)^n[1 - (1-p)^n] \tag{2.20}$$

This expression is zero for $n = 0$ and $n = \infty$, and can be shown to have a single maximum as a function of n. Thus, for a given choice of p and $\varepsilon \neq 0$ the maximum reliability is some number less than 1. A more sophisticated scheme for combining elements is therefore called for. Von Neumann discusses the theory of the majority organ at some length, with a view to overcoming this difficulty. A majority organ is a device for combining the outputs of several switches and having as its output, the switching state of the majority of the relays. Von Neumann's scheme for increasing reliability had the disappointing feature that one could not achieve a system reliability arbitrarily close to 1 unless the component relays could achieve a certain minimum performance.

Moore and Shannon [5] later re-examined the problem of von Neumann and did succeed in devising a scheme for achieving arbi- trarily high reliabilities by combining sufficient numbers of components without restriction on their reliabilities. Furthermore the design of re- liable circuits by Shannon and Moore's method is shown to lead to high reliabilities with far fewer elements; (the authors state that in the range of reliabilities for which von Neumann's design would require redundancies of 50, 000 to 70, 000 relays, their own designs require redundancies of only 80 to 120). There are very special cases in which von Neumann's circuits require fewer elements but these involve very high reliabilities, the figure cited being $1-10^{-14, 000}$.

In the course of this work Shannon and Moore derive a result of general interest for networks of identical elements. Let p be the reliability of a single element and $R(p)$ be the reliability of the system. Then it is shown that

$$\sqrt{\frac{n[1-R(p)] R(p)}{p(1-p)}} \geq \frac{dR}{dp} > \frac{R(p)[1-R(p)]}{p(1-p)} \qquad 0 < p < 1 \tag{2.21}$$

where n is the number of elements in the network. Further results on the reliability function for networks of identical, independent elements, are given by Moskowitz and McLean [M6], and in reference [B11].

Having noted that redundancy per se does not increase reliability, it would be natural next to discuss the optimum number of redundant elements for a given element, and an optimal way to introduce redundancy on all levels for a given system. The most elementary question that can be examined is how many redundant elements should be added to a single element, without further specification of the system in which the element is to be found. This is a practical problem not only in the context of relays, but also because any complex of redundant elements requires sensing and switching apparatus which itself introduces the possibility of errors in a network. Gordon, [G4], has discussed some of the implications of redundancy considering two types of errors, basing his numerical results on an equation of the form of Eq. (2.20). Druzhinin, [D5] has examined the two failure situation in continuous time and derived optimal redundancy criteria as a function of the length of time of operation of the circuit. It is possible to find the optimal value of redundancy for a single element through the use of Eq. (2.20). A simple calculation shows that N_0 , the optimum number of redundant units in the system is given by the largest value of n such that

$$(1 - \rho)^n > \frac{\varepsilon}{\varepsilon + \rho - \varepsilon\rho} \ . \tag{2.22}$$

The reliability associated with this value of N_0 is approximately

$$R \sim \frac{(1-\varepsilon)^{N_0}\rho}{\varepsilon + \rho - \varepsilon\rho} \ . \tag{2.23}$$

There has been relatively little work done specifically on the reliability of communications systems, although much of the work on error-correcting codes is directly applicable to any discussion of reliability. The simplest system that has been discussed was introduced by Goldman, [G3]. Consider a system capable of transmitting any one of n messages. Let the probability that it is desired to transmit message i be p_i . Let the probability that a message i transmitted will be received as message j be q_{ij} . It is now possible to define reliability to be the probability that a transmitted message will be received correctly, that is

$$R = \sum_i p_i q_{ii} \ . \tag{2.24}$$

However, this definition would not do justice to our expectation that if a system merely permutes letters, it has a reliability equal to 1. To remedy this defect we define an output matrix $Q*$ with elements

q^*_{ij} such that if message i is received it is identified with a letter j transmitted with probability q^*_{ij}. The matrix Q^* is obviously a Markov matrix. We can now define the reliability to be

$$R = \max_{Q^*} \sum_{i,j} p_i \, q_{ij} \, q^*_{ji} = \max_{Q^*} Tr(\underline{P} Q Q^*)$$

$$= \max_{Q^*} Tr(Q^* \underline{P} \, Q) \qquad (2.25)$$

where $Q = (q_{ij})$ and $\underline{P} = diag(p_i)$. From the last line of this equation it is evident that Q^* can be chosen as an incidence matrix (a matrix consisting of 0's and 1's) with the element 1 in the jth row occurring at the position of any maximum element of the jth column of $\underline{P} Q$. It is easily shown that with the definition of R indicated by Eq. (2.25) we must have

$$R \geq 1/n , \qquad (2.26)$$

since Q^* can be chosen to have all of its elements equal to $1/n$. If the prior probabilities p_i are unknown, but the system characteristics specified by Q are known then Q^* need not be an incidence matrix but its elements can be found by a game-theoretic analysis, [W5]. A major gap in this area of investigation is a theory which takes account of correlation and redundancy of language in the definition of reliability.

This formulation of reliability in communications systems suggests that there is a fruitful area for contact between reliability theory and information theory. We have only considered a very simple type of error correction in the definition of R given in Eq. (2.25). Clearly more sophisticated coding procedures could raise the reliability potential of a given system.

III. Time Dependent Reliability

So far we have discussed the reliability of mechanisms which are called on to perform no more than once. In this section we will describe models for the failure history of mechanisms as a function of time. All of the results of the last section with the exception of Eq. (2.20) remain valid when the reliability, R_j, of a single component is replaced by a function of time $R_j(t)$. However, several new elements are now added to reliability problems when we agree to consider the possibility of different maintenance procedures, such as inspection, repair, and replacement of defective and non-defective components. Furthermore, we may no longer be concerned with single failures only but can ask for the rate of failure production with a single system. Somewhat more practical problems involve reliability development, i.e., the estimation of the reliability of a component under development when the underlying failure mechanisms are assumed to change as a function of the development process. A rich variety of problems is therefore suggested when time dependent behavior is considered to be a focal point.

In what follows we will, as before, be concerned mainly with models of failure, omitting any discussion of estimation problems.

Let us consider, for the moment, a single component. The reliability of this component will be denoted by $R(t)$ and is generally assumed to have the properties:

$$R(0) = 1 \quad, \quad R(\infty) = 0 \quad, \tag{3.1}$$

and $R(t)$ is monotone nonincreasing in the interval $(0, \infty)$. The failure density will be denoted by $\rho(t)$, which is related to $R(t)$ by

$$\rho(t) = -R'(t) \quad, \tag{3.2}$$

assuming that the derivative exists. By definition $\rho(t) dt$ is the probability that a mechanism installed at $t = 0$ will fail at some time in $(t, t+dt)$. The probability that a mechanism will fail in $(t, t+\Delta)$, given that it is operable at time t, is $P(t, \Delta)$; i.e.

$$P(t, \Delta) = \frac{R(t) - R(t+\Delta)}{R(t)} \quad. \tag{3.3}$$

The limit of $\dfrac{P(t, \Delta)}{\Delta}$ as $\Delta \to 0$ (provided it exists), is known as the hazard rate or force of mortality, $h(t)$,

$$h(t) = \frac{\rho(t)}{R(t)} \quad. \tag{3.4}$$

Using the definition of $\rho(t)$ given in Eq. (3.2) we find that $R(t)$ can also be written in terms of the hazard rate as

$$R(t) = \exp\left(-\int_0^t h(\tau) d\tau\right) \quad. \tag{3.5}$$

Thus the assumption of Eq. (3.1) is equivalent to the statement that $\int_0^\infty h(t) dt$ diverges. The moments of the failure time are defined by

$$\overline{t^n} = \int_0^\infty t^n \rho(t) dt = n\int_0^\infty t^{n-1} R(t) dt \quad. \tag{3.6}$$

Some reliability functions which have been used in equipment studies are, [Z1], [M7], [B19]

1. Exponential distribution, $R(t) = \exp(-\lambda t)$, $\lambda > 0$

    $h(t) = \lambda$

    $$\overline{t^n} = n!/\lambda^n \tag{3.7a}$$

2. Gamma distribution, $R(t) = \dfrac{1}{\Gamma(m+1)} \displaystyle\int_{\lambda t}^{\infty} u^m e^{-u} du$, $m > -1$, $\lambda > 0$

    $$h(t) = \frac{\lambda^{m+1} t^m}{\Gamma(m+1)} \cdot \frac{e^{-\lambda t}}{R(t)} \tag{3.7b}$$

    $$\overline{t^n} = \frac{\Gamma(m+n+1)}{\Gamma(m+1)} \frac{1}{\lambda^n}$$

3. Weibull distribution, $R(t) = \exp(-t^{\alpha}/\theta)$, α, $\theta > 0$

    $h(t) = \alpha t^{\alpha-1}/\theta$

    $$\overline{t^n} = \Gamma(\frac{n}{\alpha} + 1)\, \theta^{n/\alpha} \tag{3.7c}$$

4. Truncated normal distribution

    $$\rho(t) = \frac{\alpha\varphi\{\alpha(t-t_0)\}}{\Phi(\alpha t_0)} \qquad \alpha > 0 , \qquad -\infty < t_0 < \infty$$

    where $\varphi(x) = \dfrac{1}{\sqrt{2\pi}} e^{-x^2/2}$, $\Phi(x) = \dfrac{1}{\sqrt{2\pi}} \displaystyle\int_{-\infty}^{x} e^{-u^2/2} du$

    $$h(t) = \frac{\alpha\varphi\{\alpha(t-t_0)\}}{\Phi\{-\alpha(t-t_0)\}}$$

    $$\overline{t} = t_0 + \frac{1}{\alpha} \frac{\varphi(\alpha t_0)}{\Phi(\alpha t_0)} \tag{3.7d}$$

    $$\overline{t^2} = t_0^2 + \frac{1}{\alpha^2} + \frac{t_0}{\alpha} \frac{\varphi(\alpha t_0)}{\Phi(\alpha t_0)}$$

5. General lifetime distribution

    $$\rho(t) = \frac{e^{-t} t^{\alpha}}{\Gamma(\alpha+1)} \sum_{n=0}^{\infty} a_n L_n^{\alpha}(t) , \quad \alpha > -1, \ a_0 = 1 \tag{3.7e}$$

    where the $L_n^{\alpha}(t)$ are generalized Laguerre polynomials

    $$L_n^{\alpha}(t) = \sum_{j=0}^{n} \binom{n+\alpha}{n-j} \frac{(-t)^j}{j!}$$

$$R(t) = \sum_{n=0}^{\infty} \binom{n+\alpha}{\alpha} a_n \sum_{j=0}^{n} (-1)^j \binom{n}{j} U_j(t)$$

$$h(t) = \Gamma(\alpha+1) \frac{\rho(t)}{\displaystyle\sum_{n=0}^{\infty} a_n \sum_{j=0}^{n} \binom{n+\alpha}{n-j} \frac{(-1)^j}{j!} U_j(t)}$$

$$\overline{t^n} = \frac{\Gamma(n+\alpha+1)}{\Gamma(\alpha+1)} \sum_{j=0}^{n} (-1)^j \binom{n}{j} a_j \quad .$$

where a_n are suitable parameters and the $U_j(t)$ are incomplete gamma functions defined by

$$U_j(t) = \frac{1}{\Gamma(\alpha+j+1)} \int_{t}^{\infty} u^{\alpha+j} e^{-u} du \quad .$$

Many other reliability functions have been proposed based on empirical studies, mathematical convenience, and as a result of more fundamental theoretical models for breakdown phenomenon, [B12]. The exponential distribution is widely used, often when there is slender, if any, evidence for its validity in the given situation. Many references are made to a paper by Davis, [D1], in which failure data on various network components tend to substantiate the hypothesis of exponential reliability functions. Many test programs which have been prescribed by the Department of Defense for contractors are based on the hypothesis of an exponential reliability function, and there is a large body of estimation theory based on the exponential reliability function, cf. for example, [E1-4]. However the assumption of an exponential distribution can lead to serious errors if the underlying distribution is a Weibull, [Z1]. In an early study Brown and Flood [B19] proposed the gamma type III distribution for life data on tumbler mortality. Cox, [C4] has proposed and analyzed a distribution which is the sum of two exponentials.

Just as a central limit theory of some generality exists and appears to lend some theoretical basis to the use of the normal law in many statistical procedures, so does a limit theorem for the distribution of positive random variables appear to favor the use of an exponential lifetime distribution (although uncritical application of any theorem can obviously lead to gross error). The ideas behind the theorem to be discussed can be found in the work of Palm, [P1], and Cox and Smith, [C3], but the most extensive treatment of the problem has recently been given by Drenick, [D4]. He considers a mechanism

composed of N components each of which is subject to failure independent of the other components. Assume that component i has a
hazard rate $h_i(t)$, and define a quantity $\bar{h}_N$ by

$$\bar{h}_N = \sum_{i=1}^{N} h_i(0) .$$
(3.8)

We define $R_i(t)$ to be the reliability function of component i
and $R(t) = \Pi_i R_i(t)$.

Then under the following circumstances:

1) $h_i(t) = h_i(0) + \alpha_i O(t^\theta)$ as $t \to 0$, $\theta > 0$, $i = 1, 2, \ldots, N$

2) $\bar{h}_N \to \infty$ as $N \to \infty$

3) There exists a constant A such that $|\bar{h}_N \sum_i \alpha_i| < A$, the overall
   reliability function for the mechanism will
   approach an exponential. More specifically the conclusion of the
   theorem can be stated

$$\lim_{N \to \infty} R(\tau/\bar{h}_N) = e^{-\tau}$$
(3.9)

or $R(\tau) \to \exp(-\bar{h}_N \tau)$ as $N \to \infty$, for each $\tau > 0$.

The conditions (1)-(3) are quite restrictive and are not, for example, satisfied by $R_i(t) = \exp(-\alpha_i t^2)$. Somewhat less restrictive
conditions are needed to specify the limiting residual reliability function, that is, the probability of survival for at least t units of time
of the mechanism when time is measured from some arbitrarily selected
moment of time given that the mechanism is in an equilibrium state
with respect to failures. It is easily shown, [C3], that this quantity
is related to the reliability function for an individual component by

$$G_i(t) = \frac{1}{T_i} \int_t^{\infty} R_i(x)\, dx$$
(3.10)

where T_i is the mean time to failure of the ith component. Define
$\bar{T}_N$ by

$$1/\bar{T}_N = \sum_{i=1}^{N} (1/T_i) .$$
(3.11)

Then Drenick shows that under the assumptions

(1) $\lim_{N \to \infty} \sup_{1 \le i \le N} \bar{T}_N/T_i = 0$

(2) $1 - R_i(t) \leq a_i t^\delta$ as $t \to 0$ $(a_i > 0, \delta > 0, i = 1, 2, \ldots N)$

(3) There exists an A such that $a_i \leq A$, the residual survival of the mechanism is given in the limit by

$$\lim_{N \to \infty} G(\bar{T}_N \tau) = \exp(-\tau) \qquad (3.12)$$

for each $\tau > 0$, where $G(x) = \prod_i G_i(x)$. If each of the $R_i(t)$ were identically an exponential function then Eq. (3.12) would be true for all N and τ, identically. The conditions given for this part of the theorem do not exclude any reasonable functions from consideration. The first condition simply implies that there are no components with very small times to failure.

Drenick has also considered correction terms to the limiting formulae, and finds that the convergence to the limit goes like N^{-1} rather than $N^{-\frac{1}{2}}$ as in the usual central limit theory, [G2]. Much work remains to be done in weakening the hypotheses of Drenick's theorems, particularly in regard to the underlying assumption of independent failures. Somewhat different conditions for convergence of a distribution to a negative exponential distribution are given by Ososkov, [O1].

The exponential reliability function has a constant failure rate $h(t) = \lambda$, which implies that failures occur at random and do not depend on past history. A more flexible choice of hazard functions is permitted by the family of Weibull distributions. Referring to Eq. (3.7c) in the tabulation above, we see that if $\alpha > 1$ the hazard is an increasing function of time while if $\alpha < 1$ it is a decreasing function of time. The truncated normal distribution has an increasing hazard rate. A commonly accepted picture of the hazard rate for vacuum tubes is shown in Fig. 3. Initially the hazard rate is quite high; the period from $t = 0$

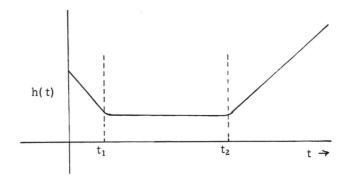

Figure 3. Generic Hazard Function

to $t = t_1$ is known as the period of infant mortality. When t satisfies $t_1 \leq t \leq t_2$ the hazard rate is sensibly constant and the failures follow a completely random pattern. The period $t > t_2$ is known as the wear-out period and is characterized by an indefinitely increasing hazard rate. Flehinger, [F4], has presented extensive results for a hazard rate of the form

$$h(t) = \alpha + \beta t^m \qquad (3.13)$$

for $m = 1$ and 2. Drenick, [D3], mentions a hazard rate of the form

$$h(t) = \begin{cases} \alpha & \text{for } t \leq t_0 \\ \alpha + \beta(t-t_0) & \text{for } t > t_0 \end{cases} \qquad (3.14)$$

although no further results are given. It has been found that a normal reliability function best describes the wearout characteristics of light bulbs while many cases of metal fatigue are best described by the Weibull distribution, [D1]. Recently Barlow has investigated the properties of probability distributions with increasing hazard rates, i.e., for which $h(t_1) \leq h(t_2)$ whenever $t_1 \leq t_2$. In some as yet unpublished work he has shown that the hypothesis of an increasing hazard rate permits one to put bounds on the reliability function and its moments. (See the paper by Barlow in this volume.)

There are many phenomenological models available for breakdown processes, which relate the reliability function of a system to more fundamental physical parameters which characterize the system. For example consider a system which consists initially of N identical, independently functioning components. Assume that the probability that a single one of these components fails in $(t, t+dt)$ is $h(t) dt$ where $h(t)$ can express a dependence on external loading conditions. It is now natural to characterize the system by n, the number of components which survive till at least time t. Let $P_n(t)$ be the probability that there are n functioning components at time t. The $P_n(t)$ are given by

$$P_n(t) = \binom{N}{n} R^n(t) [1-R(t)]^{N-n} \qquad (3.15)$$

where $R(t)$ is the reliability function for a single component,

$$R(t) = \exp\left(- \int_0^t h(\tau) d\tau\right) . \qquad (3.16)$$

The expected number of surviving machines at time t is

$$M(t) = NR(t) . \qquad (3.17)$$

The probability that the system will first reach state k in $(t, t+dt)$ is given by

$$- \sum_{j=k+1}^{N} \dot{P}_j(t) = \sum_{j=0}^{k} \dot{P}_j(t) \quad . \tag{3.18}$$

When $\lambda(t) = \lambda$, a constant hazard rate, the mean first passage time from state k can be evaluated in the form

$$\bar{t}_k = \int_0^\infty t \dot{P}_k(t) \, dt = \frac{1}{\lambda} \left(\frac{1}{k+1} + \frac{1}{k+2} + \cdots + \frac{1}{N} \right) \quad . \tag{3.19}$$

This case corresponds to N independent components in parallel, each with a negative exponential reliability function. A model, which is similar in spirit, is one for which the probability of failure of a single one of n identical components in $(t, t+dt)$ is given by $h(t)/n$. That is to say, there is a "load" which is shared by all of the surviving components. For this case we define

$$\theta(t) = \int_0^t h(\tau) \, d\tau \quad . \tag{3.20}$$

Then a solution of the equations characterizing the system,

$$\dot{P}_N(t) = - h(t) P_N(t)$$

$$\dot{P}_n(t) = h(t) [P_{n+1}(t) - P_n(t)] \quad n = 1, 2, \ldots N-1 \tag{3.21}$$

$$\dot{P}_0 = h(t) P_1(t)$$

is

$$P_n(t) = e^{-\theta(t)} \frac{[\theta(t)]^{N-n}}{(N-n)!} \quad n = 1, 2, \ldots N$$

$$P_0(t) = 1 - e^{-\theta(t)} \sum_{k=0}^{N-1} \frac{\theta^k(t)}{k!} \quad . \tag{3.22}$$

The expected number of surviving components at time t is

$$M(t) = e^{-\theta(t)} \left[N \sum_{k=0}^{N} \frac{\theta^k(t)}{k!} - \theta(t) \sum_{k=1}^{N} \frac{\theta^{k-1}(t)}{(k-1)!} \right] \quad . \tag{3.23}$$

IV. Renewal Theory and Some Applications

A principal reason for studying time-dependent reliability phe-
nomena is to be able to discuss maintenance problems with a view to
minimizing whatever costs are relevant to the operation of a given
system. Therefore the emphasis must now be shifted from properties
solely of the components of a given system, to properties which involve both the system and the management of the system. Before proceeding to a detailed analysis of some special replacement models,
we will discuss some of the renewal properties of systems which
involve random breakdowns. The results to be summarized here can
then be applied to the analysis of repair and replacement policies.

Let us begin by considering a single component, or system which
must be kept continually functioning, and which is subject to random
failures. We will assume that the failures are instantly detectable
and the failed components can be instantly replaced. Then the relevant operating history is specified by a sequence of times $\{t_i\}$,
where $t_0 = 0$ and t_i is the time of the ith failure. The simplest
system, for which a good deal of information is readily available, is
that for which it is assumed that the time intervals between successive failures $\{T_i\} = \{t_i - t_{i-1}\}$ are independent random variables for
which the reliability functions

$$R_1(t) = \Pr(T_1 > t)$$

$$R(t) = \Pr(T_k > t) \quad k = 2, 3, \ldots \qquad (4.1)$$

are known. Let $N(t)$ be the number of failures in time t. Then it
is of interest to know the distribution of $N(t)$; even a knowledge
of the moments of $N(t)$ is of great interest. The behavior of these
moments has been widely studied, (cf. [S3], for an excellent list of
references) particularly in the limit $t \to \infty$. In what follows we shall
let the kth moment, $E\{N^k(t)\}$, be denoted by $M_k(t)$. We further
define a set of functions $F_k(t)$ to be

$$F_k(t) = \Pr(t_k \le t). \qquad (4.2)$$

We shall assume the existence of the probability densities $f_k(t)$
which are defined by

$$f_k(t)dt = \Pr\{t \le t_k \le t + dt\} \qquad (4.3)$$

and which are related to the $F_k(t)$ by $f_k(t) = F'_k(t)$. If $F_k(t)$ has
a discontinuity we may still use the $f_k(t)$ providing that we allow
delta functions. More pathological behavior of the $F_k(t)$ does not
ordinarily exist in the context of reliability theory, and will not be

treated here.

It is evident from the definitions of Eqs. (4. 1), (4. 3) and (3. 2), that the $f_k(t)$ satisfy

$$f_1(t) = \rho_1(t)$$
$$f_k(t) = \int_0^t f_{k-1}(\tau)\,\rho(t-\tau)\,d\tau \qquad (4.4)$$

from which the succeeding $f_k(t)$ can be derived. If we introduce Laplace transforms:

$$f_k^*(s) = \int_0^\infty e^{-st} f_k(t)\,dt \;, \qquad \rho*(s) = \int_0^\infty e^{-st}\rho(t)\,dt \;,$$

$$\rho_1^*(s) = \int_0^\infty e^{-st}\rho_1(t)\,dt \;;$$

then the recurrence relation of Eq. (4. 4) yields the relations

$$f_k^*(s) = \rho_1^*(s)\,[\rho*(s)]^{k-1} \;. \qquad (4.5)$$

The formal expressions for the moments in terms of the $F_n(t)$ are

$$M_k(t) = \sum_{n=0}^\infty n^k [F_n(t) - F_{n+1}(t)]$$

$$= \sum_{n=1}^\infty [n^k - (n-1)^k] F_n(t) \;. \qquad (4.6)$$

A derivation of the equations for the moments is most easily carried out in terms of Laplace transforms. For example if $M*_1(s) = \int_0^\infty e^{-st} M_1(t)\,dt$, then

$$M*_1(s) = \sum_{n=1}^\infty F*_n(s) = \frac{1}{s}\sum_{n=1}^\infty f_n^*(s) = \frac{\rho_1^*(s)}{s[1-\rho*(s)]} \qquad (4.7)$$

which implies the equation in the time domain

$$M_1(t) = 1 - R_1(t) + \int_0^t M_1(\tau)\,\rho(t-\tau)\,d\tau \;. \qquad (4.8)$$

The equation for the Laplace transform of the second moment is

$$M_2^*(s) = \sum_{n=1}^\infty (2n-1) F_n^*(s)$$

$$= \frac{2\overset{*}{\rho_1}(s)}{s(1-\rho*(s))^2} - M*_1(s) \qquad (4.9)$$

$$= M*_1(s) \left(\frac{1+\rho*(s)}{1-\rho*(s)}\right)$$

or

$$M_2(t) = \int_0^t M_1(\tau)\left(1+\rho(t-\tau)\right)d\tau + \int_0^t M_2(\tau)\,\rho(t-\tau)\,dt \quad . \qquad (4.10)$$

All of the equations for the higher moments can be similarly written in terms of $M_1(t)$. Most of the attention in theoretical studies of renewal theory has been devoted to discussing the asymptotic behavior of the random variable $N(t)$ and the $M_k(t)$. The first fairly exhaustive rigorous analysis of the asymptotic behavior of $M_1(t)$ was given by Feller in 1941, [F1], by using Tauberian theorems for Laplace transforms of the $M_k(t)$. Other proofs of similar results have since been given, [S3], by specifically probabilistic methods rather than strictly analytic means, but the Laplace transform approach is convenient in that it can also give the corrections to asymptotic results. Defining

$$\overline{t^k} = -\int_0^\infty t^k dR(t) = \int_0^\infty t^k \rho(t)\,dt \quad , \qquad (4.11)$$

we can write some of the better known of the asymptotic results:

$$M_1(t) = \frac{t}{\mu_1} + \frac{\mu_2}{2\mu_1^2} - 1 + o(1) \quad \text{as } t \to \infty$$

$$\text{var}\left(N(t)\right) = \frac{\mu_2-\mu_1^2}{\mu_1^3}\,t + \left(\frac{5\mu_2^2}{4\mu_1^4} - \frac{2\mu_3}{3\mu_1^3} - \frac{\mu_2}{2\mu_1^2}\right) + o(1) \quad \text{as } t \to \infty$$

$$(4.12)$$

when the relevant moments are finite. One can also prove the result, [S3],

$$\Pr\left\{ N(t) \geq \frac{t}{\mu_1} - \frac{\alpha\sigma}{\mu_1}\sqrt{\frac{t}{\mu_1}}\right\} \to \frac{1}{\sqrt{2\pi}}\int_{-\infty}^{\alpha} e^{-y^2/2}dy \quad , \quad \text{as } t \to \infty \quad . \quad (4.13)$$

Smith has also mentioned asymptotic estimates for $p_n(t) = F_n(t) - F_{n+1}(t)$ for large n by means of the steepest descent method.

There are many obvious applications of renewal theory to the theory of reliability, and many studies of maintenance problems begin with a renewal-theoretic formulation. Before proceeding to an account of the work on maintenance and replacements, we will examine the very simplest case; namely that specified by $R_1(t) = R(t) = \exp(-\lambda t)$. Then it is simple to verify that

$$F^*_k(s) = \frac{1}{s}(\frac{\lambda}{\lambda+s})^k \tag{4.14}$$

or

$$F_k(t) = 1 - e^{-\lambda t}(1 + \lambda t + \frac{(\lambda t)^2}{2!} + \cdots + \frac{(\lambda t)^{k-1}}{(k-1)!}) \quad . \tag{4.15}$$

Furthermore $M_1^*(s) = \lambda/s^2$, or as an exact result,

$$M_1(t) = \lambda t \quad . \tag{4.16}$$

Thus, for the case of an exponential reliability function, the expected number of failures is <u>exactly</u> given by t/μ_1 whereas this is an asymptotic result for other reliability functions.

A quantity of some interest in reliability applications is the age distribution with frequency function (or density) $a_t(x)$ defined by

$a_t(x) dx = \Pr\{$System in use at t has an age A satisfying $x \leq A \leq x+dx\}$.

Notice that $a_t(x) = 0$ when $x > t$. In what follows let us assume the existence of a failure density function $\rho(t) = -R'(t)$ which is non-zero in $(0, \infty)$. This is sufficient to guarantee the existence of a function $\omega(t)$ defined by

$$\omega(t) = \frac{dM_1}{dt} \quad . \tag{4.17}$$

Moreover $\omega(t) dt$ has an interpretation as the probability that an on-line failure occurs in the time interval $(t, t+dt)$. This can be seen directly. If we <u>define</u> $\omega(t) dt$ to be this probability then $\omega(t)$ satisfies

$$\omega(t) = \rho_1(t) + \int_0^t \omega(\tau) \rho(t-\tau) d\tau \tag{4.18}$$

and the relation of Eq. (4.17) can then be proven. It can be shown that under quite general conditions, [Fl],

$$\lim_{t \to \infty} \omega(t) = \frac{1}{\mu_1} \quad . \tag{4.19}$$

It is now possible to find $a_t(x)$ in terms of known functions. There are two terms in the expression for $a_t(x)$. The first term allows for the possibility that $x = t$ and the second takes into account the contribution from $x < t$. The expression for $a_t(x)$ is

$$a_t(x) = \delta(x-t) R_1(t) + \omega(t-x) R(x) , \tag{4.20}$$

where $\delta(x-t)$ is the Dirac delta function. [1]

In the limit $t = \infty$ we find for the equilibrium age distribution,

$$a_\infty(x) = \frac{R(x)}{\mu_1} \qquad (4.21)$$

where we have used Eq. (4.19). The moments of the age distribution can be written

$$\nu_n(t) = t^n R_1(t) + \int_0^t x^n \omega(t-x) R(x) \, dx$$

$$= t^n R_1(t) + \mu_n(t) \qquad (4.22)$$

where $\mu_n(t)$ is defined to be the convolution integral appearing in this equation. If we express the Laplace transform of $\omega(t)$ in terms of those for $\rho_1(t)$ and $\rho(t)$ from Eq. (4.18), then we find for the Laplace transform of $\mu_n(t)$

$$\mu_n^*(s) = (-1)^n \frac{\rho_1^*(s)}{1-\rho^*(s)} \frac{d^n}{ds^n} \left(\frac{1-\rho^*(s)}{s} \right) . \qquad (4.23)$$

For the equilibrium age distribution of Eq. (4.21) we find

$$\nu_n = \frac{1}{(n+1)} \frac{\mu_{n+1}}{\mu_1} \qquad (4.24)$$

where the μ_n are moments of $\rho(t)$ as in (4.11). As an example of the use of Eq. (4.23) consider the simple case of $R_1(t) = R(t) = \exp(-\lambda t)$. Then

$$\mu_n^*(s) = \frac{\lambda n!}{s(s+\lambda)^{n+1}} \qquad (4.25)$$

leading to an expression for the moments

$$\nu_n(t) = \int_0^t \tau^n e^{-\lambda \tau} d\tau + t^n e^{-\lambda t} . \qquad (4.26)$$

The application of the renewal theory to reliability problems is almost immediate, provided that we identify the regeneration points with system or component breakdowns. In many situations to which renewal theory is applied it is necessary to specify several states of the system or component, e.g., for a component which breaks down and is repaired one might be interested in knowing the statistical properties of the working periods and the repair periods. We shall first discuss the simplest situations for which it is not necessary to specify several states to describe the system, and return to the more general case later.

---

1. The delta function, $\delta(t)$, is a function in the sense of the theory of distributions, [L1], with the property $\int_{-\infty}^{\infty} f(t) \delta(t) \, dt = f(0)$.

The simplest interesting situation that can be envisaged is one in which a single component is to be kept in continuous operation. The component is subject to a single type of failure, and upon failure is immediately replaced by a component with the same reliability function.[2] From the results of renewal theory given above, we know that in the limit of long times of observation (long in comparison to the mean time to failure of a single component) the expected number of replacements is t/μ_1 plus correction terms which are easily computed. Furthermore the variance is as shown in Eq. (4.12), and the distribution function for the number of replacements is asymptotically normal, as described by Eq. (4.13). Hunter and Proschan, [H1], have made a detailed study of the operation of an element with reliability function $R(t) = \exp(-t/T)$ in which they assume that the element is removed at some time Δ if it has not already failed. Among other things they find expressions in closed form for the probability of n removals in time t , of m failures in time t , and the expected values associated with these random variables.

Now let us make the situation somewhat more interesting by introducing preventive maintenance procedures. To begin with, we will consider the case of the infinite time horizon, i.e., the case in which the object is to keep a component in use continuously. The simplest type of maintenance policy is the periodic one in which replacements are scheduled every Δ units of time. If a failure occurs, the failed unit is replaced by one with the same reliability function, and replacements are rescheduled to occur Δ units of time after the occurrence of the failure. We will consider a slightly more general policy, [W3], in which replacements are scheduled in accordance with a scheduling density $g(t)$ such that

g(t) dt = Pr{replacement occurs T time units after the last failure or replacement, where $t < T \leq t + dt$, conditional on no intervening failure }.

The special choice $g(t) = \delta(t-\Delta)$ suffices to deal with strictly periodic replacement. Let $S(t)$ be the system reliability and $R(t)$ be the component reliability. The system reliability function $S(t)$ then satisfies an integral equation of the renewal type. Define the quantities

$$U(t) = R(t) \int_{t}^{\infty} g(x)\, dx$$

$$V(t) = R(t) g(t) .$$

(4.27)

Then the equation for $S(t)$ is

2. It is almost immediate that if the components are selected from a population whose members have reliability functions $R(\lambda, t)$ where λ is a random parameter then, in what follows, $R(t)$ is to be replaced by $<R(\lambda, t)>_\lambda$ where "$< >_\lambda$" means "average with respect to λ".

$$S(t) = U(t) + \int_0^t V(\tau) S(t-\tau)\, d\tau \quad . \tag{4.28}$$

This is derived by noting that if the system is operative at time t then either it is still operative before the first preventive replacement, or the first preventive replacement took place at a time τ and the first system survived for at least a time $t-\tau$. If we define the Laplace transforms:

$$S*(s) = \int_0^\infty e^{-st} S(t)\, dt \quad , \quad U*(s) = \int_0^\infty e^{-st} U(t)\, dt \quad ,$$

$$V*(s) = \int_0^\infty e^{-st} V(t)\, dt \quad ; \tag{4.29}$$

then

$$S*(s) = \frac{U*(s)}{1 - V*(s)} \quad . \tag{4.30}$$

In particular, this relation may be used as a moment generating function for the moments of system lifetime, from which we derive the results

$$\overline{t^n} = (-1)^{n-1}\, n\, \frac{d^{n-1}}{ds^{n-1}} S*(s)\Big|_{s=0+} \quad ,$$

$$\overline{t} = \frac{U*(0)}{1-V*(0)} \quad , \tag{4.31}$$

$$\overline{t^2} = -2\left[\frac{[1-V*(0)]U*'(0) + U*(0)V*'(0)}{(1-V*(0))^2}\right] ,$$

where, for example, $U*'(0)$ is the derivative of $U*(s)$ at $s = 0$. For the periodic replacement policy, $g(t) = \delta(t-\Delta)$, we find

$$U(t) = R(t) \qquad t < \Delta$$

$$= 0 \qquad t \geq \Delta$$

$$V(t) = R(t)\delta(t-\Delta) \quad , \tag{4.32}$$

which yields

$$\overline{t} = \frac{\int_0^\Delta R(t)\, dt}{1-R(\Delta)}$$

$$\overline{t^2} = \frac{2\int_0^\Delta t R(t)\, dt}{1-R(\Delta)} + \frac{2\Delta R(\Delta)\int_0^\Delta R(t)\, dt}{[1-R(\Delta)]^2} \quad . \tag{4.33}$$

As a specific illustration of these formulae, consider the failure time statistics for a system of n components in parallel, each element of which has a reliability function $R(t) = \exp(-t/T)$. The expected time to failure of this system is

$$\bar{t}_s = T(1 + \frac{1}{2} + \frac{1}{3} + \cdots + \frac{1}{n})$$ (4.34)

which is asymptotic to $\log n$ in the limit of large n. A strictly periodic replacement program leads to the expected time of failure

$$\bar{t}_s = T \frac{B_n(1 - e^{-\Delta/T})}{(1 - e^{-\Delta/T})^n}$$ (4.35)

where

$$B_n(x) = x + \frac{x^2}{2} + \cdots + \frac{x^n}{n}.$$ (4.36)

Since $B_n(x)$ approaches a limit for n becoming large, and x less than one, the mean time to failure goes up approximately exponentially with the number of redundant elements. If one considers the random replacement policy described by $g(t) = (1/T^*) \exp(-t/T^*)$ then the mean time to failure is

$$\bar{t}_s = T^* \left\{ \prod_{j=1}^{n} (1 + \frac{1}{j} \frac{T}{T^*}) - 1 \right\}.$$ (4.37)

When the condition $T \ll T^*$ is met, the mean time to failure is roughly logarithmic in n, as might be expected from the fact that maintenance replacements are seldom made. When the condition $T \gg nT^*$ is satisfied, the mean time to failure is approximately

$$\bar{t}_s \sim T^* \frac{(T/T^*)^n}{n!}.$$ (4.38)

A number of problems relating to the general maintenance system discussed in the last paragraph have been examined by Brender, [B16]. He discusses the statistics of the number of consecutive maintenance exchanges before a failure occurs, and derives renewal equations for the moments of these statistics. Some of his results, however, can be derived by more elementary considerations. As an example, the probability that n maintenance exchanges are made and then a failure occurs is given by θ_n where

$$\theta_n = [\int_0^\infty R(t) g(t) dt]^n [1 - \int_0^\infty R(t) g(t) dt],$$ (4.39)

since $\int_0^\infty R(t)g(t)dt$ is the probability that a component will survive till replacement.   Brender also discusses similar questions for finite time
intervals.

Results so far given have all related to the case where detection
of failures was instantaneous and where repairs or replacements could
be made instantaneously.   In many situations the amount of down time
due either to scheduled maintenance procedures or to repair times can
be of great importance.   We will therefore describe some of the simpler
results known for the two state or on-off mechanism.   Most of what
follows is abstracted from a survey article by Barlow and Hunter, [B2],
who summarize and extend earlier work on this subject by Takacs,
[T1].   Some of problems of interest in connection with the two state
system are:

1. What is the probability that the system will be on time t ?
2. What is the probability that it will be on t or more hours
    in a given time interval (0, T) ?
3. What is the probability distribution of the number of failures
    during a given time interval?

As is the case for many other problems which can be analyzed by renewal theoretic techniques, it is simplest to get asymptotic results
for the moment of the distributions, while the more complete results
can only be found formally in terms of Laplace transforms.

For simplicity we will refer to the two states of the system as
"operation" and "repair" and label these by subscripts 0 and 1 respectively.   Let r(t) be the probability density for repair times (r(t) can
possibly consist of delta functions), and let $w_i(t)$ be the probability
density for the occurrence of the event "end of a stay in state i". We
will assume that at t = 0 the system begins a stay in state 0 .   Then
the following integral equations are easy to establish:

$$w_0(t) \;=\; \rho(t) + \int_0^t w_1(\tau)\,\rho(t-\tau)\,d\tau$$

$$w_1(t) \;=\; \int_0^t w_0(\tau)\,r(t-\tau)\,d\tau \quad . \tag{4.40}$$

The first of these, for example, is derived by noting that the occurrence
of the end of a stay in state 0 is either the first, or a repair had
ended at time τ and the last stay in an operative state lasted t-τ
units of time.   The expected number of departures from state 0 is just

$$M_0(t) \;=\; \int_0^t w_0(\tau)\,d\tau \tag{4.41}$$

and asymptotic results are obtainable for the behavior of $w_0(t)$, $w_1(t)$, and $M_0(t)$ by a simple extension of the methods of renewal theory. If we denote by $\eta(t)$ the probability that the system is in state 0 at time t, then

$$\eta(t) = R(t) + \int_0^t w(\tau) R(t-\tau) d\tau \quad , \tag{4.42}$$

so that a knowledge of $w_1(t)$ suffices to determine the state probabilities. The detailed analysis shows that for $t \to \infty$ the functions $w_0(t)$, $w_1(t)$, and $\eta(t)$ have the asymptotic form (subject to mild restrictions which are always obeyed by reliability functions for real mechanisms)

$$w_0(t), w_1(t) = \frac{1}{\bar{t}_0 + \bar{t}_r} + o(1) \quad , \quad M_0(t) = \frac{t}{\bar{t}_0 + \bar{t}_r} + o(1)$$

$$\eta(t) = \frac{\bar{t}_0}{\bar{t}_0 + \bar{t}_r} + o(1) \tag{4.43}$$

where

$$\bar{t}_0 = \int_0^\infty t p(t) dt \quad , \quad \bar{t}_r = \int_0^\infty t r(t) dt \quad . \tag{4.44}$$

A straightforward recourse to the strong law of large numbers is sufficient to obtain the results of Eq. (4.43), but by examining the expansion of the Laplace transforms of Eqs. (4.40) and (4.42), it is possible to find the correction terms in the asymptotic expansions. Barlow and Hunter's paper also contains an expression for the Laplace transform of the distribution of the number of failures in time t.

    An important result, first derived by Takacs, [T1], giving the probability that the amount of down time in an interval $(0, t)$, is less than x is also cited by Barlow and Hunter. Let $\beta(t)$ be the amount of down time in time t, and let

$$\Omega(t, x) = \Pr\{\beta(t) \leq x\} \quad . \tag{4.45}$$

Let

$$A(t) = \int_0^t r(\tau) d\tau \tag{4.46}$$

be the probability that a repair takes t units of time or less and let us denote by $[G(t)]^{*n}$ the n-fold Stieltjes convolution, where by the two-fold Stieltjes convolution we mean the following:

$$[G(t)]^{*2} = \int_0^t G(t-x) dG(x) \quad . \tag{4.47}$$

Then Takacs has shown that

$$\Omega(t, x) = \sum_{n=0}^{\infty} [A(x)]^{*n} \{[1-R(t-x)]^{*n} - [1-R(t-x)]^{*(n+1)}\} . \qquad (4.48)$$

Of somewhat greater practical interest is the asymptotic result proven by Takacs for the distribution of $\beta(t)$. If we let T be the expected value of the time spent in a single occurrence of the operational state, σ^2 be the variance, and T_r and σ_r^2 be the same parameters for a single occurrence of down time, then Takacs' result is:

$$\lim_{t \to \infty} \left\{ \frac{\beta(t) - \dfrac{T_r t}{T + T_r}}{\sqrt{\dfrac{T_r^2 \sigma^2 + T^2 \sigma_r^2}{(T+T_r)^3}} t} \le x \right\} = \frac{1}{\sqrt{2\pi}} \int_{-\infty}^{x} \exp(-\frac{u^2}{2}) du . \qquad (4.49)$$

Finally, an exact result can be obtained for $\Omega(t, x)$ when $R(t) = \exp(-t/T)$ and $A(t) = \exp(-t/T_r)$. This result is

$$\Omega(t, x) = e^{-\frac{(t-x)}{T}} \left[1 + \sqrt{\frac{t-x}{TT_r}} \int_0^x e^{-y/T_r} y^{-\frac{1}{2}} I_1\left([4(t-x)y/TT_r]^{\frac{1}{2}}\right) dy\right]$$

$$(4.50)$$

where $I_1(x)$ is a Bessel function of imaginary argument.

A recent paper, [W7], treats a generalization of the two state system. It is assumed that the system can be in any one of N operative states, the time spent in any one state being a random variable, with the reliability function for the element depending on the state. It is also assumed that transitions between states take place in accordance with a Markov chain. Such a model is of some interest with reference to systems which are subjected to varying environments, or in which stored components can deteriorate in storage as well as in use. A number of models of this general nature can be treated by specific applications of the theory of semi-Markov processes.

V.   Maintenance Policies

Although it is usually of a good deal of interest in any application to know the failure characteristics of a system, it is of greater importance to be able to determine policy with regard to the operation, maintenance, and replacement of components. Up till this point we have simply described system reliability in terms of the topological arrangement of the circuit, or as a function of time. We have further discussed some of the modifications which are necessary in the theory when periodic or random replacements are made. Our purpose in the following paragraphs will be to survey some of the literature on maintenance and replacement problems. Although these problems are not new, it is only in recent years that a concerted effort has been made to develop a general mathematical theory of maintenance procedures when the components and systems are subject to failure.

The principle feature which will distinguish this section from those past is the inclusion of costs and gains in the various models. These may be ill-defined in many situations, nevertheless it is sometimes possible to draw quantitative conclusions from very general properties of the cost function. In other cases the costs may be well-defined: then the problem before the analyst is to provide a suitable mathematical framework in which it is possible to perform numerical calculations. The types of problems to be discussed will fall into two rough categories. The first is related to inventory theory, and pertains to the optimal supply of spare parts or redundant elements for a system. The second problem type refers to inspection procedures and replacement policies. This latter category encompasses problems with many different types of constraints. We can only hope to mention a small number of these in the present article.

The first question to be discussed may be called the spare parts, or optimal kit problem. One of the most widely discussed problems in this area concerns the best method for introducing redundant elements into a system which consists of a number of elements in series. Supposing that there are two elements in series and two replica elements, there are two possible ways to introduce redundancy, as illustrated in Fig. 4. It has been shown that if switching is perfect, the optimum way to introduce redundancy is at the lowest level, i.e., add the redundant elements to the individual elements rather than to larger units in the system, [F3]. The simplest question that can be tackled which takes economic factors into account in an elementary way, concerns a series network of elements with reliabilities $R_1, R_2, \ldots R_N$. It is assumed that an element of type j costs C_j . The problem is to find the method of adding redundant elements which will result in the greatest reliability while keeping the total cost less than a given amount C . This formulation leads to the maximization of a reliability R given by

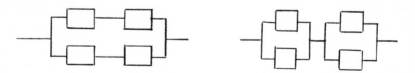

Figure 4. Two methods for introducing redundancy.

$$R = \prod_{j=1}^{N} [1 - (1-R_j)^{n_j}] \qquad (5.1)$$

with respect to $\{n_j\}$ subject to the constraint

$$\sum_{j=1}^{N} n_j C_j \leq C \qquad (5.2)$$

or an equivalent inequality if the cost is not a linear function of the C_j. In general this problem is a difficult example in the theory of non-linear programming and an answer in closed form cannot be given. This problem has been treated by Mine, [M4] and others, both under the approximation that the n are continuous variables and under the approximation that the n are discrete. In the former case he assumes that the equality in Eq. (5.2) is valid, and shows that the problem can be reduced to the solution of a single transcendental equation for the Lagrange multiplier. In the latter case Mine gives an algorithm for finding the optimum redundancy vector $\{n_j\}$. The solution to the continuous case can be written

$$n_j = \frac{1}{\log(1-R_j)} \log \left[\frac{\lambda C_j}{\lambda C_j + \log(1/(1-R_j))} \right] \qquad (5.3)$$

where λ is the solution to the equation resulting from the simplified cost relation $\Sigma n_j C_j = C$. When the components are initially very reliable ($R_j \sim 1$) the value of λ is approximately given by

$$\lambda = e^{C - \left\{ \prod_i \left(\frac{C_j}{\log \frac{1}{1-R_j}} \right)^{\frac{1}{\log(1-R_j)}} \right\}^{\frac{1}{\Sigma_j [\log(1-R_j)]}} - 1} ; \qquad (5.4)$$

while when the components were initially unreliable ($R_j \sim 0$) the value of λ is approximately equal to N/C.

Bellman and Dreyfus, [B8], have applied the method of dynamic programming, but the solution is given in terms of an algorithm only, and is best suited for computer calculation. Flehinger, [F3], has discussed the optimal redundancy problem for certain relay systems which include sensing and switching mechanisms. The methods employed were graphical and no approximation schemes were mentioned. A problem related to the optimal redundancy problem has been treated by Albert and Proschan, [A1]. Their model also is that of a series of components with individual reliabilities $R_1, R_2, \ldots R_N$ and a system

reliability R equal to their product. It is desired to raise the system
reliability R* by raising the component reliabilities to new levels
$R_1 *, R_2 *, \ldots R_N^*$. The cost of raising an individual R_j to R_j^* is
assumed to be a known function $G_j(R_j, R_j^*)$ and the total cost is
assumed to be the sum

$$G(R, R*) = \sum_{i=1}^{N} G_i(R_i, R_i^*) . \qquad (5.5)$$

In order to obtain an algorithm for the solution, Albert and Proschan
make the mild restriction that $G_i(R, e^x)$ is a strictly convex, increasing function of x having a continuous first derivative for $0 \leq R \leq e^x < 1$.
If we set $f_i(x) = G_i(R_i, e^x)$, and for $\lambda \geq 0$ we define

$$r_i(\lambda) = \begin{cases} \ln R_i & \text{if } f'_i(\ln R_i) > \lambda \\ 0 & \text{if } f'_i(0) \leq \lambda \\ x \text{ such that } f'_i(x) = x & \text{otherwise} \end{cases} \qquad (5.6)$$

and $r(\lambda) = \sum_{i=1}^{N} r_i(\lambda)$. If $r = \ln R*$, and $\lambda*$ is the minimum value
of λ such that $r(\lambda) = r$, then

$$R_i^* = e^{r_i(\lambda*)} \qquad (5.7)$$

minimizes the total effort required to achieve a system reliability
of R* .

Proschan and his collaborators have made extensive studies of the
optimal spare parts problem when the components have reliabilities
which are a function of time, [P2-P4, B1, B13, B14]. The problem
which they treat is the determination of the number of spare parts of
each type of component of a system required to give a specified as-
surance of continued operation during a given period at minimum cost
for spares. In one of the first papers on this subject Black and Proschan assume that a period of operation is defined by having d_{ij} components of type i receiving t_j hours of operation. It is assumed
that the components of type i have a reliability function of the form
$R_i(t) = \exp(-\mu_i t)$, and that a spare of type i costs C_i units of
money. The solution algorithm for the case of independent components
in series (i.e., there must be at least one component of each type
functioning for the specified period in order that the system function)
is quite similar to that cited above, since the time dependence is
rendered a non essential part of the problem, given the fixed times t_j .

The results of this first paper have since been extended in various
directions. The most important extension has been to show that the
solution algorithm is valid for a wider class of underlying reliability
functions than the exponential. Proschan, [P2], has shown that the
method of solution is valid whenever the underlying failure densities
are PF_2 (Polya frequency function of type 2) , that is, the $f(t)$ have
the property

$$
\begin{vmatrix}
f(x_1 - y_1) & f(x_1 - y_2) \\
f(x_2 - y_1) & f(x_2 - y_2)
\end{vmatrix}
\geq 0
\qquad\qquad (5.8)
$$

where $x_1 < x_2$ and $y_1 < y_2$. Another characterization of PF_2 functions is that

$$
\frac{f(t-\Delta)}{f(t)}
$$

is non decreasing in t for all $\Delta \geq 0$. The class of PF_2 functions
is an important one for reliability applications since it can be shown,
[Kl], that a PF_2 function has an increasing hazard rate (the reverse
is not necessarily true) . A further extension of the theory of spare
parts problem has been to the case of periodic resupply, [P3]. In
this paper, however, the solution is only discussed for the exponential reliability function. The results given are of simple enough form
to be of practical utility.

One of the earliest statements of the regenerative maintenance
problem in the context of reliability was made by N.R. Campbell, [Cl],
although earlier investigations in inventory theory had posed similar
questions. Campbell's paper contains a discussion of the comparative
advantages of replacing a number of elements (in his particular case,
these were street lamps) either en masse, or as they failed. While
the question raised is interesting, the treatment, which does not use
some of the general results of renewal theory, is not of wide validity.
Nevertheless the paper is of some interest as a precursor of much of
the more recent investigations. Campbell's problem differs from most
problems of current interest in that he does not require immediate replacement to be made when a failure occurs.

We will begin our account of the theory with a description of a
problem first treated by Savage, [S2], and more recently in a slightly
different formulation, by Barlow, Hunter, and Proschan, [B7]. Savage
supposes that it is desired to replace a set of elements at a sequence
of times $\{t_i\}$, that the cost of replacing these elements is A and
that $F(T)$ is a loss function if the time between two successive replacements is T . This cost function is supposed to be expressed
in units of cost and to be related in some way to the probability of

failure or deterioration of the elements during the operating interval.
It is then required to find some optimal sequence of replacement times
$\{t_i\}$ such that the average loss per unit time, defined by

$$C = \lim_{n \to \infty} \frac{\sum_{i=1}^{n} [A + F(t_i - t_{i-1})]}{t_n} \qquad (5.9)$$

is a minimum. Savage considers only the case where $F(x)/x$ tends
to infinity as x tends to infinity. Under the assumption that $F(x)$
is continuous, non-negative, nondecreasing, and $F(0) = 0$ it is
easily proven that C assumes its minimum value. If $F(x)$ is dif-
ferentiable then the critical equation is

$$A + F(x) - xF'(x) = 0 . \qquad (5.10)$$

If $F(x)$ is convex there exists a unique solution. It is shown that
there are cases in which the solution set contains more than one element, and is not necessarily unique. When A and $F(x)$ are random
variables, as is usually the case, the same treatment of the problem
holds, providing that expected values are used.

Barlow, Proschan, and Hunter in [B1], treat a somewhat less
general version of this problem by specifying a form for the cost
function. The situation is described in terms of a checking problem.
One wishes to specify the optimum checking time for some equipment,
given that a single check entails a cost C_1 and a failure in the system in the interval between inspections will cost C_2 units of money
per unit of undiscovered failure time. The failure density will be
$\rho(t)$, as before, and the expected loss is then

$$L = \sum_{k=0}^{\infty} \int_{x_k}^{x_{k+1}} [(k+1)C_1 + (x_{k+1} - t)C_2]\rho(t)\,dt . \qquad (5.11)$$

The optimal checking times are chosen to minimize L. Only when
$\rho(t)$ is exponential are the x_k integral multiples of a single period.
Otherwise, the result of setting

$$\frac{\partial L}{\partial x_k} = 0 \qquad k = 1, 2, \ldots \qquad (5.12)$$

is the recursion relation

$$x_{k+1} = x_k + \frac{R(x_{k-1}) - R(x_k)}{\rho(x_k)} - \frac{c_1}{c_2} \qquad (5.13)$$

from which, given x_1 (it being assumed that $x_0 = 0$), one can calculate the remaining x_k. If $R(t)$ is PF_2 and x_1 is chosen too small
the x_k sequence will eventually become negative; if x_1 is
chosen too large the sequence $\{x_{k+1} - x_k\}$ will eventually increase.
Hence a unique minimizing value of x_1 can be chosen. In practice
this may be quite difficult to find and it is therefore of some interest
to restrict attention to the subclass of periodic checking policies.

Most theoretical work to date has in fact been done on periodic
maintenance policies assuming an infinite usage horizon. All of them
start in some form from the relation for the expected cost as a function
of time

$$C(t, \Delta) = C_1 E\{N_1(t, \Delta)\} + C_2 E\{N_2(t, \Delta)\} \qquad (5.14)$$

where C_1 is the cost of a replacement, C_2 the cost of a failure,
$N_1(t, \Delta)$ the number of replacements in time t, $N_2(t, \Delta)$ the
number of failures in time t, and Δ is the maintenance period
which must be solved for. The criterion usually chosen is to set
$dD/d\Delta$ equal to zero where

$$D(\Delta) = \lim_{t \to \infty} C(t, \Delta)/t . \qquad (5.15)$$

The existence of the limit is guaranteed by the fundamental theorems
of renewal theory or by the strong law of large numbers. Notice that
C_1 and C_2 can be generalized costs measured in money, time, or
any other penalties that might be relevant to the system. A fairly
comprehensive account of this type of theory is given in [B5]. Earlier
work on restricted forms of the periodic maintenance problem are also
to be found in [W4]. All of the results mentioned above in connection
with renewal theory can obviously be used in the calculation of
$C(t, \Delta)$; all that need be done is to calculate the quantities
$E\{N_1(t, \Delta)\}$, $E\{N_2(t, \Delta)\}$ for each particular model. The paper by
Barlow and Proschan, [B1], is a careful exposition of periodic and
random maintenance problems. In it they prove that for continuous
$R(t)$ Eq. (5.15) actually attains its minimum over Δ. It is further
shown that for an infinite time horizon there always exists a strictly
periodic replacement policy which is superior to a random policy.

We will not present some of the specific results which are applicable to the study of maintenance and replacement policies. For
periodic replacement policies in which failures are instantly detected
it can be shown, [W4], that $D(\Delta)$, the asymptotic cost per unit
time is given by

$$D(\Delta) = \frac{(C_1 - C_2) R(\Delta) + C_2}{(t_1 - t_2) R(\Delta) + t_2 + \int_0^{\Delta} R(t) dt} \qquad (5.16)$$

where t_1 is the expected time required for a maintenance replacement and t_2 is the expected time required for the replacement of a failed unit. The cost per unit of <u>operating</u> time is

$$D_0(\Delta) = \frac{(C_1 - C_2)R(\Delta) + C_2}{\int_0^\Delta R(t)\,dt} . \qquad (5.17)$$

It should be noted that Eq. (5.16) does not necessarily have a minimum. When $\Delta = 0$ is the solution for the optimum value of Δ in Eq. (5.16) the elements are clearly of no economic value. The value of the expected cost per unit of operating time, $D_0(\Delta)$ always has a minimum when $C_2 > C_1$, since $D_0(0) = \infty$ and $D_0(\Delta)$ is manifestly positive. Of course $\Delta = \infty$ might be the optimal period. Several special cases of the minimization of Eqs. (5.16) and (5.17) are presented in [B3] and [W4]. A sufficient condition for a finite minimum of the expected cost per unit operating time to exist is that the hazard rate at $\Delta = \infty$ satisfy

$$h(\infty) > D_0(\infty)/(C_2 - C_1) . \qquad (5.18)$$

Barlow and Proschan, [B1], outline a theory of sequential replacement policies for the case of a finite time horizon. They show that for a finite time horizon there exists policies which require that after each removal the next planned replacement interval is selected to minimize expected expenditure during the remaining time, and that these policies will be more effective than a fixed replacement policy. An algorithm is given for determining the optimal policy but it requires machine computation for each particular case.

Barlow and Hunter, [B3], applied a variation of the analysis given in the last paragraph in a discussion of the relative merits of two types of policies for an infinite time horizon system:

I: Perform preventive maintenance after Δ hours of operation without failure. When a system failure occurs, perform system maintenance and reschedule the time for preventive maintenance.

II: Perform preventive maintenance on the system after it has been operating a total of Δ units of time regardless of the number of intervening failures. The problem is formally equivalent to that treated by Campbell in [C1]. Barlow and Hunter take as their criterion for determining the optimum maintenance period for the two policies, the optimization of the asymptotic expected fractional amount of time that the system is on. If we assign the costs

$C_1 = T_s$ = expected time for the performance of a scheduled maintenance

$C_2 = T_e$ = expected time for the performance of an emergency maintenance

in Eq. (5.17) and set[3] $dD_0(\Delta)/d\Delta = 0$, the minimizing equation can be written

$$h(\Delta) \int_0^\Delta R(t)\, dt + R(t) = \frac{T_e}{T_e - T_s} \tag{5.19}$$

where $h(t)$ is the hazard rate. Under an optimal type I policy the asymptotic efficiency becomes

$$\eta(\Delta) = \begin{cases} \dfrac{\mu_1}{\mu_1 + T_e} & T_e \leq T_s \\[3mm] \dfrac{1}{1 + (T_e - T_s) h(\Delta)} & T_e > T_s \end{cases} \tag{5.20}$$

where μ_1 is the mean time to failure. For the treatment of a policy of Type II Barlow and Hunter assume that after each failure only minimal repair is made so that the system's hazard rate is not disturbed, and that the system is returned to its original state after preventive maintenance. The efficiency, $\eta(\Delta)$, can be shown to be

$$\eta(\Delta) = \frac{\Delta}{T_m \int_0^\Delta h(t)\, dt + T_s + \Delta} \tag{5.21}$$

where T_m is the time required to perform minimal repair. The equation which leads to a maximizing value of Δ is

$$\int_0^\Delta t h'(t)\, dt = T_s/T_m \tag{5.22}$$

which has a unique solution if $h(t)$ is strictly increasing to infinity. The efficiency under optimal conditions is

$$\eta(\Delta) = \frac{1}{1 + T_m h(\Delta)} \tag{5.23}$$

when $T_e = T_s$ the two policies are easily compared and it can be proved that policy I is better than policy II if

$$T_m > \frac{T_s}{\mu_1 h(\mu_1)} . \tag{5.24}$$

---

3. We can write Eq. (5.17) in the form $D_0(\Delta) = T_d/T_0$ where T_d is the expected value of a single period of down time, and T_0 is the expected value of a single period of operating time. The asymptotic efficiency (i.e., Barlow and Hunters' criterion) is $\eta(\Delta)$ where

$$\eta(\Delta) = \frac{T_0}{T_d + T_0} = \frac{1}{1 + D_0(\Delta)}$$

hence minimizing $D_0(\Delta)$ is equivalent to maximizing $\eta(\Delta)$.

A similar situation has been investigated by slightly more sophisticated methods, in [W8]. An element is given with the reliability
function $R(t) = \exp(-t/T)$ and it is desired to conduct checks every
Δ units of time to determine whether or not the element is operative.
It is assumed that the inspection time is a random variable with mean
equal to t_i and the time to repair or replace the mechanism is a random variable with expectation t_r. A further assumption is that surveillance may be imperfect, and is characterized by a parameter θ
which is the probability of detecting a faulty mechanism. It is shown
by the asymptotic results in the theory of semi-Markov processes that
the asymptotic availability, or probability of being in a state of operability is

$$\eta = \frac{\theta}{\theta\lambda_r + (1 + \frac{\theta w}{1-w})(\lambda_i + \log\frac{1}{w})} \qquad (5.25)$$

where

$$\lambda_r = t_r/T \ , \quad \lambda_i = t_i/T \ , \quad w = \exp(-\Delta/T) \ . \qquad (5.26)$$

The optimal value for Δ is the solution to

$$\frac{(1-w)^2}{w} + \theta(1 - w - \log\frac{1}{w}) = \theta\lambda_i \ . \qquad (5.27)$$

When λ_i is small, as it is apt to be in practice, an optimal value for
Δ is found by noting that if λ_i were exactly equal to zero then the
solution to Eq. (5.27) is $w = 1$ or $\Delta = 0$. If one expands w as a
power series in Δ/T and retains lowest terms only then an approximate solution is

$$\Delta \sim T\sqrt{\frac{2\theta\lambda_i}{2-\theta}} \qquad (5.28)$$

and the approximate value for the availability when this value of Δ
is used is

$$\eta \sim \frac{1}{1+\lambda_r} - \frac{1}{(1+\lambda_r)^2}\sqrt{\frac{\lambda_i(2-\theta)}{2\theta}} \qquad (5.29)$$

when θ is not too close to zero. The first term is the result which
would be given by the usual renewal theoretic argument, for a zero
inspection time and the second term is the modification introduced by
a finite inspection time. This model can be generalized to deal with
reliability functions other than the exponential, but the resulting equations for the determination of Δ are quite complicated.[4] It is also

---

4. It should be pointed out that for a non exponential reliability func-
    tion one can always do better with an optimal sequence of inspec-
    tion times that are not necessarily uniformly spaced. However the
    case of a uniformly spaced Δ is clearly of the greatest interest.

possible to treat the case in which the inspection time is a random variable which is described by a probability distribution with disposable parameters, and the results for this case are given in [W8]. Coleman and Abrams, [C2] have recently analyzed a somewhat more general case in which they allow for a false alarm rate (calling a good system bad) and for the probability of equipment failure during the checkout. Let α denote the probability of calling a good system bad; let q denote the probability of a failure during a checkout period, and p_c denote the probability of a failure occurring before the actual test if the failure occurs during a checkout period. Then (in our notation) their result is

$$\eta = \frac{\theta(1-w)}{(\log \frac{1}{w}+\lambda_i)(1+w[q(1-\alpha+\alpha p_c-p_c\theta)-(1-\theta)]+\lambda_r[1-(1-q)(1-\alpha)w]}$$

$$(5.30)$$

This result reduces to Eq. (5.25) when $\alpha = q = 0$. The most complete exposition of inspection policies for systems with an exponential reliability function has been given in an unpublished Rand memorandum by Kamins, [K2].

A thesis by Flehinger, [F5], contains an account of the theory of several types of maintenance policies. The four types of policies that are studied are:

1. Block changes, in which components of a given type are replaced simultaneously, at times determined by a renewal process.
2. Preventive replacement on the basis of age.
3. System checkouts, in which a component is used intermittently. A component which fails during a period of non use does not induce system failure until it is called into use.
4. Marginal testing, in which components may be in one of several states. If a component is discovered to be in a critical (but necessarily a failure) state it is preventively replaced.

For systems which are maintained according to these policies, Flehinger calculates the functions $A(x;y)$ and $B(x;y)$ which are defined as follows:

$A(x;y)$ = Pr{component is preventively removed by x | installation at y , measured from the last preventive removal}

$B(x;y)$ = Pr{component induces a system failure by x | installation at y} .

The principal results for these models are stated as a number of integral equations when the functions $A(x;y)$ and $B(x;y)$ are assumed known. We will summarize Flehinger's results here. We define the functions

$M(t)$ = Expected number of successive failures in $(0, t)$ before the first preventive removal.

$G(t)$ = Probability that a component which enters the system at 0 is preventively removed in $(0, t)$.

$U_p(t)$ = Expected number of preventive removals in $(0, t)$.

$U_f(t)$ = Expected number of failure removals in $(0, t)$.

$R(t; x)$ = Probability of us failure removal in $(s, x+t)$.

Flehinger shows that $M(t)$ is the unique solution of

$$M(t) = B(t, 0) + \int_0^t B(t; y) \, dM(y) \quad . \qquad (5.31)$$

Knowing $M(t)$, one can find $G(t)$ from

$$G(t) = A(t; 0) + \int_0^t A(t; y) \, dM(y) \quad . \qquad (5.32)$$

The functions $U_p(t)$ and $U_f(t)$ are determined from ordinary renewal equations:

$$U_p(t) = G(t) + \int_0^t U_p(t-\tau) \, dG(\tau)$$

$$U_f(t) = M(t) + \int_0^t M(t-\tau) \, dU_p(\tau) \quad . \qquad (5.33)$$

Finally $R(t; x)$ can be found from

$$R(t; x) = \Psi_t(x) + \int_0^x \Psi_t(x-y) \, dU_p(y) \; ; \qquad (5.34)$$

where

$$\Psi_t(x) = 1 - F(x+t; 0) + \int_0^x [1-F(x+t; y)] \, dM(y)$$
$$+ \int_0^t [1-F(t-\tau; 0) \, d_\tau a(\tau, x)] \quad , \qquad (5.35)$$

$F(x; y)$ is defined by

$$F(x; y) = A(x; y) + B(x; y) \, , \qquad (5.36)$$

and $a(\tau, x)$ is a solution of the integral equation

$$a(\tau, x) = A(x+\tau; 0) - A(x; 0) + \int_0^x [A(x+\tau; y) - A(x; y)] \, dM(y)$$
$$+ \int_0^\tau A(\tau-u; 0) \, da(u, x) \quad . \qquad (5.37)$$

The analysis of these equations is quite difficult since the initial equation in the chain, Eq. (5.31), is not in convolution form and cannot, therefore, be solved by transform methods. For any case of practical interest, numerical methods would be needed for the resolution of Eqs. (5.31) to (5.37). Therefore one can say very little about the advisability of choosing one of the four policies listed above for a given system, unless actual numerical values are known for the system parameters. Most of the results of the first part of Flehinger's thesis are contained in a recently published paper [F6].

The second part of Flehinger's thesis consists of a study of a model for marginal testing. Results are derived only for a Markovian system, although the same system could probably be treated by means of a semi-Markov analysis, thereby extending the applicability of the model. Flehinger assumes that a component can be in any one of n states, the state n being the failed state. Tests are performed at an interval of T and if the component is found to be in any one of the states k, k+1, ... n-1 it is replaced by a component in state 0. The results of this calculation are again expressible in terms of functions A(x; y) and B(x; y), but because of their relatively complicated form, will not be reproduced here. A recent paper, [W7], has considered a multistate model, in which the reliability function is different in each state. If the transitions between states can be described by a Markov chain then a formal expression can be given for the Laplace transform of the reliability function. However, detailed results for this model are not given, as they are for Flehinger's model.

The so-called repairman problems are related to maintenance problems just discussed, but results are only known for negative exponential failure distributions. In the repairman problem it is assumed that there are m machines which must be kept in continuous operation and there are r repairmen to service them upon breakdown. This type of problem arises in many guises, and a result of primary interest is that for the most economical number of repairman for the operation of the system. As might be expected most attention has been devoted to the case where repair times have a negative exponential distribution. Extensive results for this case were first given by Palm, [P1], and have been summarized in the books of Feller, [F2], Saaty, [S1], and in a paper by Naor, [N1]. If p_n is the steady state probability (i.e., the probability for $t \to \infty$) that n machines are being serviced then by solving the difference equations which describe the process it can be shown that

$$p_n = p_0 \binom{m}{n} \left(\frac{\lambda}{\mu}\right)^n \qquad\qquad 0 \le n < r$$

$$p_n = p_0 \binom{m}{n} \frac{n!}{r! \, r^{n-r}} \left(\frac{\lambda}{\mu}\right)^n \qquad r \le n \le m$$

$$\text{(5.38)}$$

$$p_0 = 1 - \sum_{n=1}^{m} p_n \qquad\qquad (5.38 \text{ cont.})$$

where μ is the parameter which appears in the distribution of repair times. Takacs, [T2], has given an explicit solution for the case of negative exponential reliability function and an arbitrary repair time distribution. The solution is quite complicated, and to date no specific practical application has been made of Takacs' general results. Apart from Takacs' investigation, Benson and Cox, [B10], and Ashcroft, [A2], have dealt with the case of a single repairman and constant repair time. A good summary of these results is given in the book by Cox and Smith, [C4].

Many variations of the basic problem are possible and have been analyzed by various authors. For example, applications in the textile industry require the solution of the problem under the assumption that the repairman walks from machine to machine and is not able to repair the machine till he arrives at it, [B9]. Other variations include an extension to repairmen with different capabilities, where a repairman has duties other than the attendance of broken machinery, and different types of failure. Taylor and Jackson, [T3], have dealt with a provisioning problem very similar to those considered by Proschan and his co-workers. They consider the problem of m engines which must operate continuously in aircraft. When an engine fails it is instantly replaced by a spare, provided that one is available, and the failed engine is immediately placed in the repair shop. Both the failure time distribution and the repair time distributions are taken to be negative exponential. It is assumed that there are n repair facilities and when n+1 engines need repair, or are being repaired, the engines stop operating until a replacement is available. The only results given by the authors are for the steady state probabilities of having k engines under repair. There are many other papers written on Markov models for maintenance systems. Just as space has prevented us from giving a more detailed review of other aspects of reliability, so we have only mentioned some of the directly relevant models from this field of study.

The article just concluded is of course incomplete and will no doubt be obsolete after a very short period of time. However, it is hoped that this short summary of recent mathematical developments in the study of reliability will serve as an introduction to the various types of problems which are of current interest, as well as indicating progress in their solution.

ACKNOWLEDGMENTS

I would like to express my thanks to Mr. George L. Beyer of the U. S. Naval Ordnance Laboratory who first roused my interest in reliability problems, and Dr. Bertrand P. Ramsay of the same laboratory, who encouraged my further investigations. I would like to thank Drs. Joan R. Rosenblatt and Alan Goldman for their careful reading of this manuscript and for several suggestions which have been incorporated into the manuscript.

REFERENCES

[A1] A. Albert, F. Proschan, "Increased reliability with minimum effort," EDL-M210, Electronic Defense Laboratory, Mountain View, California (1959).

[A2] H. Ashcroft, "The productivity of several machines under the care of one operator," J. Roy. Stat. Soc. B, 12, 145 (1950).

[B1] R. E. Barlow, F. Proschan, "Planned replacement," EDL-M296, Electronic Defense Laboratories, Mountain View, Cal. (1960).

[B2] R. E. Barlow, L. C. Hunter, "Performance of a one unit system," Proc. Fourth. Nat. Conf. on Mil. Elect., 111, (1960).

[B3] R. E. Barlow, L. C. Hunter, "Optimum preventive maintenance policies," J. Op. Res. Soc. Am. 8, 90 (1960).

[B4] R. E. Barlow, L. C. Hunter, "Mathematical models for system reliability," Sylvania Technologist, 1, 2 (1960).

[B5] R. E. Barlow, L. C. Hunter, "System efficiency and reliability," Technometrics, 2, 43 (1960).

[B6] R. E. Barlow, L. C. Hunter, "Criteria for determining optimum redundancy," IRE Trans. on Rel. and Qual. Cont. 9, 73 (1960).

[B7] R. E. Barlow, L. C. Hunter, F. Proschan, "Optimum checking procedures," Proc. Seventh Nat. Symp. on Rel. and Qual. Cont., 485 (1961).

[B8] R. Bellman, S. Dreyfus, "Dynamic programming and the reliability of multicomponent devices," J. Op. Res. Soc. Am. 6, 200 (1958).

[B9] A. Ben-Israel, P. Naor, "A problem of delayed service I, II," J. Roy. Stat. Soc. B, 22, 245, 270 (1960).

[B10] F. Benson, D. R. Cox, "The productivity of machines requiring attention at random intervals," J. Roy. Stat. Soc. B, 13, 65 (1951).

[B11] Z. W. Birnbaum, J. D. Esary, S. C. Saunders, "Multi-component structures and their reliability," Technometrics, 3, 55 (1961).

[B12] Z. W. Birnbaum, S. C. Saunders, "A Statistical model for life-length of materials," J. Am. Stat. Assoc., 53, 151 (1958).

[B13] G. Black, F. Proschan, "On optimal redundancy," J. Op. Res. Soc. Am., 7, 581, (1959).

[B14] G. Black, F. Proschan, "Spare part kits at minimum cost," IRE Proc. Fifth Nat'l Symp. on Rel. and Qual. Cont. in Elec., 281 (1959).

[B15] C. E. Bradley, E. L. Welker, "A model for scheduling maintenance utilizing measures of equipment performance," ARINC Monograph No. 8 (1959).

[B16] D. M. Brender, "The statistical dynamics of preventive replacement," IRE Wescon Convention Record (Part 6), 23 (1959).

[B17] D. M. Brender, M. Tainiter, "A Markovian model for predicting the reliability of an electronic circuit from data on component drift and failure," IBM Research Report RW-32 (1961).

[B18] P. H. Broussard, "A study of the application of Boolean algebra to system reliability," WSMR TM-142 (1954).

[B19] G. W. Brown, M. M. Flood, "Tumbler mortality," J. Am. Stat. Assoc. 42, 562 (1947).

[C1] N. R. Campbell, "The replacement of perishable members of a continually operating system," J. Roy. Stat. Soc. (Supplement) VII, 110 (1941).

[C2] J. J. Coleman, I. J. Abrams, "Mathematical model for operational readiness," J. Op. Res. Soc. Am. 10, 126 (1962).

[C3] D. R. Cox, W. L. Smith, "On the superposition of renewal processes," Biometrika 40, 1 (1953).

[C4] D. R. Cox, W. L. Smith, Queues, (John Wiley and Sons, 1961).

[C5] D. R. Cox, "The analysis of experimentally distributed life times with two types of failures," J. Roy. Stat. Soc. B, 21, 411 (1959).

[C6] R. R. Carhart, "A survey of the current status of the electronic reliability problem," RAND Research Memorandum - 1131 (1953).

[D1] D. J. Davis, "The analysis of some failure data," J. Am. Stat. Soc. 47, 113 (1952).

[D2] R. E. Drenick, "A statistical view of reliability," Proceedings of the Working Conference on the Theory of Reliability, N. Y. U. 30 (1957).

[D3] R. F. Drenick, "Mathematical aspects of the reliability problem," J. Soc. Ind. Appl. Math. 8, 125 (1960).

[D4] R. F. Drenick, "The failure law of complex equipment," J. Soc. Ind. Appl. Math. 8, 680 (1960).

[D5] D. V. Druzhinin, "Dependence of the effectiveness of redundancy on operating time of the system" (Russian), Izv. Akad. Nauk SSSR 11, 83 (1958).

[E1] B. Epstein, M. Sobel, "Life testing," J. Am. Stat. Assoc. 48, 486 (1953).

[E2] B. Epstein, M. Sobel, "Some theorems relevant to life testing from an exponential distribution," Ann. Math. Stat., 25, 373 (1954).

[E3] B. Epstein, "Truncated life tests in the exponential case," Ann. Math. Stat. 25, 555, (1954).

[E4] B. Epstein, M. Sobel, "Sequential life tests in the exponential case," Ann. Math. Stat. 26, 82, (1955).

[F1] W. Feller, "On the integral equation of renewal theory," Ann. Math. Stat. 12, 243 (1941).

[F2] W. Feller, An Introduction to Probability Theory and its Applications (John Wiley and Sons, 1957).

[F3] B. J. Flehinger, "Reliability improvement through redundancy at various system levels," IBM J. Res. and Dev., 2, 148 (1958).

[F4] B. J. Flehinger, P. A. Lewis, "Two-parameter lifetime distributions for reliability studies of renewal processes," IBM. J. Res. and Dev. 3, 58 (1959).

[F5] B. J. Flehinger, "A General Model for the Reliability Analysis of Systems Under Various Preventive Maintenance Policies," Thesis, Columbia Univ. (1960).

[F6] B. J. Flehinger, "A general model for the reliability analysis of systems under various preventive maintenance policies," Ann. Math. Stat. 33, 137 (1962).

[G1] C. R. Gates, "The reliability of redundant systems," JPL Memo 20-76 (1952).

[G2] B. V. Gnedenko, A. N. Kolmogoroff, Limit Distributions of Independent Random Variables, (Addison Wesley, Cambridge, Mass.) 1954.

[G3] S. Goldman, Information Theory (Prentice Hall, New York) 1953.

[G4] R. Gordon, "Optimum component redundancy for maximum system reliability," J. Op. Res. Soc. Am. 2, 229 (1957).

[G5] A. W. Green, A. Drummond, "Effects of maintenance techniques on the reliability of fixed communications equipment," ARINC Publication 111 (1958).

[H1] L. C. Hunter, F. Proschan, "Replacement when constant failure rate precedes wearout," Naval Res. Log. Quart. 8, 127 (1961).

[K1] S. Karlin, F. Proschan, "Polya type distributions of convolutions," Ann. Math. Stat. 31, 721 (1960).

[K2] M. Kamins, "Determining checkout intervals for systems subject
      to random failures," RM-2578, June 1960.

[L1] M. J. Lighthill, Fourier Analysis and Generalized Functions
      (Cambridge University Press, Cambridge) 1958.

[L2] W. F. Luebbert, "Principles and oncepts of reliability for
      electronic equipment and systems, Parts I, II," Electronics
      Research Laboratory Reports 90, 91, Stanford University, 1955.

[M1] C. Mack, "The efficiency of N machines unidirectionally
      patrolled by one operative when walking time is constant and
      repair times are variable," J. Roy. Stat. Soc. B 19, 173 (1957).

[M2] C. Mack, T. Murphy, N. L. Webb, "The efficiency of N machines
      uni-directionally patrolled by one operative when walking time
      and repair time are constants," J. Roy. Stat. Soc. B. 19, 166
      (1957).

[M3] R. L. Madison, "Effects of maintenance on system reliability,"
      ARINC Publication 101-16-144 (1959).

[M4] H. Mine, "Reliability of Physical System," IRE Transactions,
      PGIT, IT-5, 138, Special Supplement (1959).

[M5] E. F. Moore, C. E. Shannon, "Reliable circuits using less re-
      liable elements," J. Frank. Inst. 262, 191, 281, (1956).

[M6] F. Moskowitz, J. B. McLean, "Some reliability aspects of
      systems design," IRE Transactions PGRQC, 8, 7(1956).

[M7] W. Mendelhall, "A bibliography on life testing and related topics,"
      Biometrika 45, 521 (1958).

[N1] P. Naor, "On machine interference," J. Roy. Stat. Soc. B. 18,
      280 (1956).

[N2] J. von Neumann, "Probabilistic logics and the synthesis of
      reliable organisms from unreliable components," Automata
      Studies, 43, (Princeton Press) 1956.

[O1] G. A. Ososkov, "A limit theorem for flows of similar events,"
      Theory of Prob. and Appl. I, 248 (1956).

[P1] C. Palm, "Arbetskraftens Fördelning vid Betjäning av Automats-
      kiner," Industritidningen Norden, 75, 75, 90, 119 (1947).

[P2] F. Proschan, "Minimum cost for spares when component failure
      is not necessarily exponential," Rep. EDL-M185, Electronic
      Defense Lab., Mountain View, Cal.' (1959).

[P3] F. Proschan, "Periodic resupply policy achieving specified
      protection against system shutdown at minimum cost," Rep.

EDL-M205, Electronic Defense Laboratories, Mountain View, Cal. (1959).

[P4] F. Proschan, "Optimal system supply," Rep. EDL-E38, Electronic Defense Laboratory, Mountain View, Cal. (1960).

[R1] T. J. Runnenberg, "Machines served by a patrolling operator," Math. Cent. Amsterdam, Rep. 5221 (1957).

[S1] T. Saaty, Elements of Queueing Theory, (McGraw Hill, New York) 1961.

[S2] L. R. Savage, "Cycling," Naval Res. Log. Quart. 3, 163 (1956).

[S3] W. L. Smith, "Renewal theory and its ramifications," J. Roy. Stat. Soc. B, 2, 243 (1958).

[T1] L. Takacs, "On certain sojourn time problems in the theory of stochastic processes," Acta Math. Hung. 169 (1957).

[T2] L. Takacs, Stochastic Processes, Problems and Solutions, (Methuen, London) 1960.

[T3] J. Taylor, R. P. Jackson, "An application of the birth and death process to the provision of spare machines," Op. Res. Quart. 5, 95 (1954).

[W1] G. H. Weiss, M. M. Kleinerman, "On the reliability of networks," Proc. Nat. Elec. Conf. X, 123, (1955).

[W2] G. H. Weiss, "On the time-dependent reliability of networks," Proc. Nat. Elec. Conf. XI, 1017 (1956).

[W3] G. H. Weiss, "On the theory of replacement of machinery with a random failure time," Naval Res. Log. Quart. 3, 279 (1956).

[W4] G. H. Weiss, "On some economic factors influencing a reliability program," NAVORD 4256, U. S. Naval Ordnance Laboratory, White Oak, Md.

[W5] G. H. Weiss, "The reliability of communications systems," NAVORD 5664, U. S. Naval Ordnance Laboratory, White Oak, Md.

[W6] G. H. Weiss, M. M. Kleinerman, "The reliability of sequentially operated networks," Convention Record IRE, 6, 222 (1961).

[W7] G. H. Weiss, "The reliability of components exhibiting cumulative damage effects," Technometrics 3, 413 (1961).

[W8] G. H. Weiss, "A problem in equipment maintenance," Management Science, 8, 266 (1962).

[W9] H. K. Weiss, "Estimation of reliability growth in a complex system with a Poisson-type failure," J. Op. Res. Soc. Am. 4, 532, (1956).

[W10] E.L. Welker, "Relationship between equipment reliability,
       preventive maintenance policy, and operating costs," Proc.
       5th Nat. Symp. on Rel. and Qual. Control, 270 (1959).

[W11] O. Wing, "Reliability study of communications systems,"
       Tech. Rep. T32/B; CU-50-58-AF-677-EE. Electronic Res.
       Labs, Columbia University (1958).

[Z1]   M. Zelen, M.C. Dannemiller, "The robustness of life testing
       procedures derived from the exponential distribution," Techno-
       metrics 3, 29 (1961).

DISCUSSION OF THE PAPER BY Dr. WEISS

R. E. Barlow. I will confine my discussion to the so-called renewal quantity—$M(t)$—the expected numer of renewals in time t. I should like to make a few remarks regarding this quantity when the renewal process is generated by an IHR distribution (see references [2] and [3] of "Maintenance and Replacement Policies"). If $F(t)$ is an IHR distribution with density $f(t)$ and

$$q(t) = \frac{f(t)}{1 - F(t)}$$

then

$$t\, f(0) \leq M(t) \leq \int_0^t q(x)\, dx$$

for all t. Equality is attained with the exponential distribution. Also if μ_1 denotes the mean of $F(t)$, then

$$M(t) = t/\mu_1 \qquad \text{for all } t \leq \mu_1 .$$

Also it was noted that

$$M(t) = t/\mu_1 + \frac{\mu_2/2 - (\mu_1)^2}{(\mu_1)^2} + o(1) .$$

Since $\mu_2 \leq 2(\mu_1)^2$ when $F(t)$ is IHR, we can also conclude that

$$M(t) \leq t/\mu_1$$

for sufficiently large t.

Gene B. Parrish. Are the estimates available for the error incurred in using the method of steepest descent? I have seen the method used often in physical problems without any estimate of the error.

Dr. Weiss replied at the seminar and later submitted the following in writing:

G. Weiss. Concerning the question by Dr. Parrish, there does exist an analysis of error term for the method of steepest descents. Some of it is summarized in the book by de Bruijn on asymptotic analysis. However, there have been no applications of this type of error analysis to solutions of the renewal equation.

Dr. Barlow's consideration of functions with increasing hazard ratio is an important advance in reliability theory. However, the engineer who needs practical answers may be unsatisfied by bounds

which can be so wide as to be practically useless. Since, with re-
gards to reliability, this is not the best of all possible worlds, further
research both using particular distributions and non-parametric studies
will still continue to be informative.

FRANK PROSCHAN
Redundancy for reliability improvement

In writing an expository paper on the use of redundancy for reliability improvement, there is a certain implicit pressure to avoid excess
redundancy. I will therefore say as briefly as I can that:

(1) This paper treats just a small selection of the many
     interesting topics in redundancy.
(2) The choice reflects my own tastes and prejudice.
(3) Omission of work in redundancy is no reflection on
     its importance of quality.

1.   OPTIMUM ALLOCATION OF REDUNDANCY SUBJECT TO CONSTRAINTS

One of the most basic problems in designing for high reliability
goes as follows. Consider a system consisting of k states which
functions if and only if each stage functions. The ith stage is to
consist of n_i components in parallel, each of which has independent
probability p_i , $0 < p_i < 1$, of functioning. How shall we select
the vector of positive integers $\underline{n} = (n_1, n_2, \ldots, n_k)$ to maximize system reliability

$$R(\underline{n}) = \prod_{i=1}^{k} (1 - q_i^{n_i}) , \qquad (1.1)$$

where $q_i = 1 - p_i$, subject to the linear constraints

$$\sum_{i=1}^{k} c_{ij} n_i \leq c_j , \quad j = 1, 2, \ldots, r , \qquad (1.2)$$

where $c_{ij} > 0$ for $i = 1, 2, \ldots, k$, $j = 1, 2, \ldots, r$? We require each

$$c_j \geq \sum_{i=1}^{k} c_{ij}$$

since each n_i is at least 1 .

55

For $r = 1$, this problem has been treated by Mine [13] and Moscowitz and McLean [16] by the method of Lagrange multipliers using the approximation that the n_i are continuous variables. However, for this case, an exact solution may be obtained using an algorithm derived by Kettelle [12]. Actually, the solution may be obtained more quickly using the method described below to get close to the answer, and then using Kettelle's algorithm in the last stages of the computation. (This was first observed by Nathan Mantel.) The details of this improvement will appear in [4]. For $r = 2$, Bellman and Dreyful [5] show how to solve the problem on a computer by dynamic programming methods.

In [17], it is shown that the solution to this problem in non-linear programming may be obtained as follows:

1. For $\lambda = \lambda_1, \ldots, \lambda_r$, with each $\lambda_j > 0$, compute

$$n_i(\lambda) = \left[\frac{1}{\ln q_i} \ln \frac{\exp\left\{ \sum_{j=1}^{r} \lambda_j c_{ij} \right\} - 1}{\exp\left\{ \sum_{j=1}^{r} \lambda_j c_{ij} \right\} - q_i} \right] + 1 \ , \ i = 1, 2, \ldots, k \ , \tag{1.3}$$

where $[x]$ represents the largest integer not exceeding x . It is easy to verify that each $n_i(\lambda)$ is a non-decreasing function of each λ_j . Let $\underline{n}(\underline{\lambda}) = (n_1(\underline{\lambda}), \ldots, n_k(\underline{\lambda}))$.

2. Since $R(\underline{n})$ is a strictly increasing function of each n_i , it follows that $R(\underline{n}(\lambda))$ is a non-decreasing function of each λ_j . Thus we retain only $\underline{n}(\underline{\lambda})$ satisfying (1.4) below such that there exists no $\underline{n}(\underline{\lambda}')$ satisfying (1.4) for which $\underline{n}(\underline{\lambda}') \geq \underline{n}(\underline{\lambda})$ with strict inequality for at least one coordinate.

$$c_j \geq \sum_{i=1}^{k} c_{ij} \left\{ \left[\frac{1}{\ln q_i} \ln \frac{\exp\left\{ \sum_{j=1}^{r} \lambda_j c_{ij} \right\} - 1}{\exp\left\{ \sum_{j=1}^{r} \lambda_j c_{ij} \right\} - q_i} \right] + 1 \right\} , \ j = 1, 2, \ldots, r \ . \tag{1.4}$$

3. For each vector in the set retained compute $R(\underline{n}(\underline{\lambda}))$. The solution is that $\underline{n}(\underline{\lambda})$ for which $R(\underline{n}(\underline{\lambda}))$ is a maximum.

It should be pointed out that the solution obtained is an approximate solution, in general. In the special cases in which $\underline{c} = (c_1, \ldots, c$

happens to be such that for some $\underline{\lambda}$,

$$\sum_{i=1}^{k} c_{ij} n_i (\underline{\lambda}) = c_j \quad \text{for } j = 1, 2, \ldots, r ,$$

then the solution is exact.

To prevent unnecessary computation, we seek initial trial values of $\underline{\lambda}$ which approximately yields equality in (1.4), although it is not always possible to find such vectors $\underline{\lambda}$.

A related, somewhat more difficult, problem may be posed if, instead of redundant units all operating simultaneously, we assume a system in which redundant units are in standby condition. In this model, when an operating component fails, a standby unit of the same type, if available, is immediately switched into operation. As before, we wish to determine the number of redundant units of each type to provide, subject to a set of linear constraints.

Specifically, we assume as before a system consisting of k stages which functions if and only if each stage functions. The life of a component of type i occupying stage i is governed by the failure distribution $F_i(t)$, with all components independent. How shall we select the set of non-negative numbers n_i of redundant units, $i = 1, 2, \ldots, k$, to maximize the probability of survival until time t_0 , subject to constraints

$$\sum_{i=1}^{k} c_{ij} n_i \leq c_j , \quad j = 1, 2, \ldots, r , \tag{1.5}$$

where

$$c_{ij} > 0 , \quad c_j > 0 , \quad \text{for } i = 1, 2, \ldots, k , \quad j = 1, 2, \ldots, r ?$$

For the case $r = 1$, a solution is obtained in [18]. The nonlinear programming technique used to solve the present problem is similar to that used in the earlier problem; however, interesting differences develop because of the renewal aspects of the present redundancy problem. The case in which the underlying life distributions are exponential, $F_i(t) = 1 - e^{-\lambda_i t}$, yields an especially neat solution, since the distribution for $N(t)$, the number of failures of component type i in time t , is readily expressed in closed form as the Poisson,

$$P[N(t) \leq n] = \sum_{i=0}^{n} \frac{(\lambda t)^i}{i!} e^{-\lambda t} .$$

In [18] the solution is obtained for underlying exponential life distributions not only in the case of known parameters, but also in the case of parameters known with uncertainty; specifically, λ_i is itself a

random variable governed by the Gamma distribution. In actually calculating the solution obtained in [18] for $r = 1$ for underlying failure
distributions other than the exponential, the results of Morrison and
David [15] concerning the life distribution of systems with spares
may be helpful.

The search for the maximum of a function is generally greatly
simplified if the function is concave, since in this case only one
maximum exists. One of the fascinating features of the present problem is that the probability of system survival until time t_0 is shown
to be a concave function of n_i , the number of redundant units provided of the ith type, under the mild and reasonable restriction that
$F_i(t)$ has an increasing failure rate (conditional probability of failure, given the age). [4]

2. OPTIMUM REDUNDANCY WHEN COMPONENTS
ARE SUBJECT TO TWO KINDS OF FAILURE

A number of papers have discussed the problem of achieving optimum redundancy assuming only two component states are possible,
the operating state and the failed state. [5], [7], [8], [10], [12],
[13]. An interesting problem in planning redundancy arises if we
consider systems in which failure may take either one of two forms.

For example, consider a network of relays arranged so that there
are m subsystems in parallel, each subsystem consisting of n relays in series; we shall call such an arrangement a parallel-series
arrangement. An open circuit failure of a single relay would make the
subsystem containing it unresponsive. Analogously, we may consider
a system consisting of n subsystems in series, each subsystem containing m relays in parallel (a series-parallel arrangement). A
short circuit failure of a single relay makes the subsystem containing
it unresponsive; open circuit failure of all the relays in a subsystem
makes the entire system unresponsive. As a third example (oversim-
plified), one of several airplane autopilots in parallel may fail by no
longer functioning or by giving a command to make an extreme, destructive maneuver; the first type of failure simply removes the failed
autopilot from consideration, the second type causes system failure.
Note that in all these examples adding components will make failure
of one type more likely at the same time as it reduces the chance of
failure of the other type. Thus a valid problem exists in determining
the optimum number of components to use, even when no constraints
are present of the type described in Section 1.

2.1. Maximizing System Reliability

From these examples we may abstract the following model. A
system consists of m subsystems, each subsystem containing n
components. A component may fail in either of two mutually exclusive

ways. A type 1 failure of a single component causes the subsystem containing it to fail; in this case the subsystem failure will be called type 1. On the other hand, failure of type 2 of all the components in a subsystem causes the subsystem to fail; this subsystem failure is called failure of type 2. Moreover, failure of type 1 of all the sub-systems causes system failure, while failure of type 2 of a single subsystem causes system failure. Each component independently has probability $p_1 > 0$ of experiencing type 1 failure, $p_2 > 0$ of experi-encing type 2 failure, where $p_1 + p_2 < 1$. For given n find the value of m maximizing system reliability, i.e., the probability that the system is functioning.

For example, in the case of the parallel-series arrangement of relays, an open circuit failure of a relay would constitute a type 1 failure, while a short circuit failure of a relay would constitute a type 2 failure. On the other hand, in the case of the series-parallel ar-rangement of relays, an open circuit failure of a relay would consti-tute a type 2 failure, while a short circuit failure would constitute a type 1 failure.

Barlow and Hunter, [1], [2] obtain an approximate expression for the number of components maximizing the reliability of systems of com-ponents in parallel and of systems of components in series (corre-sponding to the case $n = 1$ above). Gordon [11] treats the same case, but maximizes a somewhat different objective function.

In the general model stated above, system reliability R can be expressed as

$$R = (1 - p_2^{n})^{m} - (1 - q_1^{n})^{m}, \qquad (2.1)$$

where $q_i = 1 - p_i$, $i = 1, 2$. As shown in [3], the value of m maxi-mizing system reliability is (without approximation) $m^* = [m_0] + 1$, where

$$m_0 = n \frac{\ln q_1 - \ln p_2}{\ln(1 - p_2^{n}) - \ln(1 - q_1^{n})}. \qquad (2.2)$$

Qualitative properties of m_0 as a function of the parameters are ob-tained in [3], such as:

(1) $\frac{m_0}{n}$ is a strictly increasing function of n ;

(2) $m_0 < 1$, $= 1$, or > 1 according as $q_1^{n} + p_2^{n} > 1$, $= 1$, or < 1 .

Making the additional Assumptions (A) below, further properties of m_0 are obtained.

Assumptions (A). Each component has independent probability $F(t)$ (right continuous and $F(0) = 0$) of failing by time t, $0 \le t < \infty$. If failure occurs, the conditional probability of type 1

failure is p , $0 < p < 1$, or type 2 failure is q , $p+q = 1$, independently of the time of failure. No repair or replacement occurs.

Under Assumptions (A), it is further shown in [3] that:

(3) m_0 is a strictly increasing function of p for
     $0 \leq p \leq 1$, $0 < F(t) < 1$.

(4) $m_0 \to n$ as $t \to 0$; $m_0 \to \dfrac{1 - q^n}{q^n}$ as $t \to \infty$.

(5) For $n = 1$, $\frac{1}{2} < p < 1$, m_0 is a strictly increasing function
     of $F(t)$.

2.2 Maximizing Expected System Life

Actually, in many cases, specifying the operating time for the
system is not feasible. Rather the system operates until it fails. In
such cases it is reasonable to maximize the expected time until system failure.

Under Assumptions (A), a solution is obtained for the case $n = 1$
and exponential failure, $F(t) = 1 - e^{-\lambda t}$, in [1], [2]. Numerical results are tabulated for the optimum number m^* up to 10. In [3], the
solution for the case $n = 1$ is extended to general distribution functions F, retaining Assumptions (A).

Define r_m as the root for p in $[0, 1]$ of

$$-\int_0^\infty \{1 - qF(t)\}^m qF(t)\, dt + \int_0^\infty \{pF(t)\}^m \{1 - pF(t)\}\, dt = 0 ;$$

r_m is shown to be unique, and to satisfy

$$.5 = r_1 < r_2 < r_3 < \ldots .$$

For $r_{m-1} < p < r_m$, the number of components yielding maximum
expected system life is m . For $p = r_m$, both m and $m+1$ yield
the maximum.

For the case of uniform failure distribution, numerical results are
tabulated in [3] for the optimum number of components up to 10.
Formulas are given to permit the calculation of the solution for general
distribution function $F(t)$, although the actual computation would un-
doubtedly be painful and tedious in general.

3. QUALITATIVE ASPECTS OF REDUNDANT SYSTEMS

In Sections 1 and 2 we have reviewed research directed toward
achieving optimum redundancy under various assumptions and restrictions. In the present situation, we survey research in redundancy
leading to general qualitative relationships true for a broad class of
systems.

This phase of the study of redundancy was initiated by Von Neumann in a fundamental paper [19] which shows how to construct more reliable basic components ("Sheffer stroke" organs) by appropriate use of relatively unreliable components. Moore and Shannon [14], inspired by the Von Neumann paper, carry out an elegant analysis for relay circuits in which they show that by the proper incorporation of redundancy, arbitrarily reliable circuits can be constructed from arbitrarily unreliable relays. Bounds are obtained on the number of elements required to achieve a specified reliability. Birnbaum, Esary and Saunders [6] generalize the concept and extend some of the results of Moore and Shannon to the class of structures (coherent structures, defined below) having the property that replacing failed components by functioning components cannot cause a functioning system to fail.

More precisely, Birnbaum, Esary and Saunders consider structures of say n components. Each component, as well as the structure itself, is either in the functioning state or failed state. Let x_i designate the state of the ith component, $x_i = 1$ indicating that the ith component is operating, $x_i = 0$ indicating that the ith component has failed. The state of the system is given by the structure function $\phi(\underline{x})$, where $\underline{x} = (x_1, x_2, \ldots, x_n)$; $\phi(\underline{x}) = 1$ indicates the structure is performing while $\phi(\underline{x}) = 0$ indicates the structure has failed. Birnbaum, Esary and Saunders define a structure function $\phi(\underline{x})$ to be coherent if

(a) $\phi(\underline{x})$ is non-decreasing in each argument,
(b) $\phi(0, 0, \ldots, 0) = 0$,
(c) $\phi(1, 1, \ldots, 1) = 1$.

Thus (a) states that the functioning of a component contributes to the functioning of the system, (b) states that if all components fail, the system must fail, and (c) states that if all components perform the system must perform.

Examples of coherent structures are:

(1) A bridge has structure function:

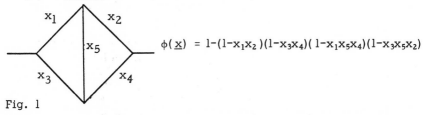

$$\phi(\underline{x}) = 1 - (1 - x_1 x_2)(1 - x_3 x_4)(1 - x_1 x_5 x_4)(1 - x_3 x_5 x_2)$$

Fig. 1

(2) A "k out of n" structure functions if and only if at least k of its n elements function. Setting k = n yields the series structure; setting k = 1 yields the parallel structure.

(3) The relay networks considered by Moore and Shannon constitute a class of coherent structures.

(4) A two-terminal network with one or more components repli-
cated, e.g.:

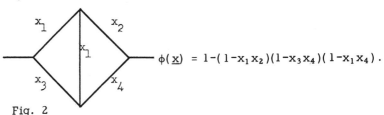

$$\phi(\underline{x}) = 1-(1-x_1 x_2)(1-x_3 x_4)(1-x_1 x_4).$$

Fig. 2

We assume that the two-components labelled x_1 either both perform
or both fail. The Moore-Shannon model does not consider replication
of components.

So far, we have been considering only the deterministic behavior
of components and structure. To study the relationship between system reliability and component reliability, we must introduce a probability distribution for the performance of components. Define the reliability of the ith component as p_i = probability that the ith component functions, and let $\underline{p} = (p_1, p_2, \ldots, p_n)$ designate the vector
of component reliabilities. Similarly, the reliability of the system
is defined as h = probability that the system functions. Assuming
independent components we may indicate system reliability as a
function $h(\underline{p})$ of component reliabilities.

3.1 Bounds on System Reliability

In general, the function $h(\underline{p})$ is messy. However, we shall
describe how to obtain upper and lower bounds for $h(\underline{p})$ for coherent
systems which are relatively convenient and of some theoretical
interest [9]. To present the bounds we shall need to define the following terms. A minimal path of a coherent structure ϕ is a subset
of components $i_1, i_2, \ldots, i_m$ such that if $\underline{x}$ is the vector with 1's
in positions $i_1, \ldots, i_m$ and o's elsewhere, we must have

(a) $\phi(\underline{x}) = 1$, and

(b) $\phi(\underline{y}) = 0$, where $\underline{y}$ is obtained from $\underline{x}$ by changing one
or more 1's into 0's. In other words, the functioning of all the ele-
ments in a minimal path insures the functioning of the system; however, if one of these functioning elements fails, the functioning of
the remaining elements in the minimal path is insufficient to guarantee
the functioning of the system. Similarly, a minimal cut is a subset
$i_1, i_2, \ldots, i_m$ such that if $\underline{x}$ is the vector with 0's in positions
$i_1, i_2, \ldots, i_m$ and 1's elsewhere, we must have

(a) $\phi(\underline{x}) = 0$, and

(b) $\phi(\underline{y}) = 1$, where $\underline{y}$ is obtained from $\underline{x}$ by changing one or more 0's into 1's. In other words, the failure of all the elements in the minimal cut insures the failure of the system; however, if one of these failed elements is converted into a functioning element, the failure of the remaining elements does not imply the failure of the system.

For example, the four minimal paths in the bridge shown in Example (1) above are $A_1 = 1, 2; A_2 = 3, 4; A_3 = 1, 5, 4; A_4 = 3, 5, 2$. Note that the structure function φ in this example is expressed as a parallel arrangement of the minimal paths, with the elements in each minimal path arranged in series.

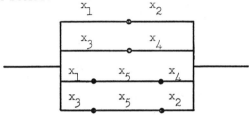

Fig. 3   Parallel arrangements of minimal
paths of bridge

In general, it is clear that the structure function φ of a coherent system may be expressed in terms of its minimal paths $A_1, A_2, \ldots, A_r$ as

$$\varphi(\underline{x}) = 1 - \prod_{j=1}^{r} \left\{ 1 - \prod_{i \in A_j} x_i \right\} , \qquad (3.1)$$

corresponding to a parallel arrangement of minimal paths $A_1, A_2, \ldots, A_r$, with the elements in each minimal path arranged in series. In a similar fashion we may express the structure φ of a coherent system in terms of its minimal cuts $B_1, B_2, \ldots, B_s$ as

$$\varphi(\underline{x}) = \prod_{k=1}^{s} \left\{ 1 - \prod_{i \in B_k} (1 - x_i) \right\} , \qquad (3.2)$$

corresponding to a series arrangement of minimal cuts $B_1, B_2, \ldots, B_s$, with the elements in each minimal cut arranged in parallel.

Thus for the bridge, Example (1) above, the four minimal cuts are $B_1 = 1, 3; B_2 = 2, 4; B_3 = 1, 5, 4; B_4 = 3, 5, 2$. We may express φ as

$$\varphi(\underline{x}) = \{1-(1-x_1)(1-x_3)\}\{1-(1-x_2)(1-x_4)\}\{1-(1-x_1)(1-x_5)(1-x_4)\}\{1-(1-x_3)(1-x_5)(1-x_2)\}.$$

It is interesting to note that elements 1, 5, 4 comprise a minimal path <u>and</u> a minimal cut, and similarly for elements 3, 5, 2.

As shown in [9], an upper bound on system reliability, $h(\underline{p})$, may be obtained from the minimal path representation (3.1) by replacing each x_i by the corresponding p_i, assuming independent components with respective reliabilities $p_1, p_2, \ldots, p_n$. Similarly, a lower bound may be obtained from the minimal cut representation (3.2) by replacing each x_i by the corresponding p_i. Specifically, we obtain

$$\prod_{k=1}^{s}\left(1 - \prod_{i \in B_k} q_i\right) \le h(\underline{p}) \le 1 - \prod_{j=1}^{r}\left(1 - \prod_{i \in A_j} p_i\right) , \qquad (3.3)$$

where, as usual, $q_i = 1 - p_i$, $i = 1, 2, \ldots, n$. Intuitively, we may justify (3.3) as follows. If a given component appears in more than one minimal path, then naturally such replications of the component will all function or all fail, since only one component is actually present. The upper bound in (3.3) corresponds to the system reliability if such replications were actually physically present, operating independently of each other. The lower bound in (3.3) may be similarly justified.

Theoretically, the bounds are interesting since they permit us to approximate complex systems by systems having only parallel and series arrangements. Practically, (3.3) is useful since often it permits us to obtain readily upper and lower bounds on the reliability of complicated systems whose minimal paths and cuts can be readily determined by inspection.

As an example, consider the two-terminal network with structure shown in Fig. 4.

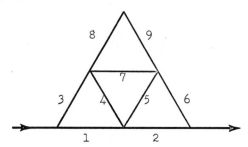

Fig. 4 Two-terminal network

The minimal paths are readily seen to be:

12	156	1476	14896	342
3456	376	3752	3896	38952.

Similarly, the minimal cuts are:

13	1478	1479	1456
2543	2578	2579	26 .

From these minimal paths and minimal cuts we immediately obtain in the case of like components, using (3.3):

$$h_L(p) \leq h(p) \leq h_U(p) \quad ,$$

where

$$h_L(p) = (1-q^2)^2(1-q^4)^6 \quad , \text{ and}$$

$$h_U(p) = 1 - (1-p^2)(1-p^3)^3(1-p^4)^4(1-p^5)^2 \ .$$

Fig. 5 shows graphically $h(p)$, $h_L(p)$, and $h_U(p)$.

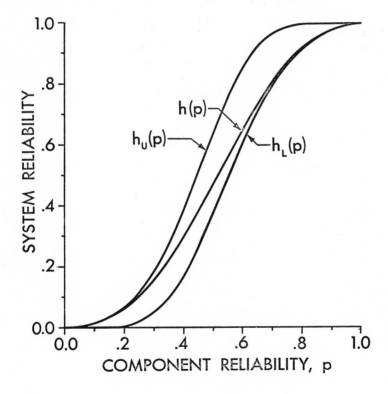

Fig. 5 Bounds on system Reliability for a Two-terminal Network

3.2 S-Shape of Reliability Function

A fascinating aspect of redundancy is revealed in studying the shape of the system reliability function h(p) under the assumption of independent components with common reliability p . Moore and Shannon initiate this line of research in [14] as a means of establishing that arbitrarily reliable relay networks may be constructed from arbitrarily crummy relays. (In their paper "crummy" is a convenient designation for the state more technically labelled as "lousy.") Birnbaum, Esary, and Saunders show in [6] that the same qualitative result concerning the shape of the reliability function applies to coherent systems. Finally, Esary and Proschan [9] extend the result to a limited degree to systems of components of differing reliabilities.

Let us first see why Moore and Shannon are interested in the shape of h(p) . They suppose like idealized relays are subject to two kinds of failure: failure to close and failure to open. Similarly, circuits constructed from these relays are subject to two kinds of failure: failure to close, i.e., no closed path is achieved from input wire to output wire when the circuit is commanded to close, and failure to open, i.e., a closed path exists from input wire to output wire even though the circuit is commanded to open. They assume each relay operates independently of the others with probability p_1 (preferably small) of closing when commanded to open (non-energized) and probability p_2 (preferably large) of closing when commanded to close (energized). These probabilities do not vary with time. The basic problem is to achieve a probability $h(p_1)$, sufficiently small, of the circuit being closed when commanded to be open, and a probability $h(p_2)$ sufficiently large of the circuit being closed when commanded to be closed, by appropriate arrangement of a sufficient number of primitive units.

It soon becomes clear that the analysis may be conducted more simply by studying h(p) , the probability of circuit closure, as a function of p , the common probability of individual relay closure. For p small (corresponding to a non-energized relay) we would hope to achieve a value h(p) < p , while for p large (corresponding to an energized relay) we would hope to achieve a value h(p) > p . Thus the relay circuit represents an improvement in reliability over the individual relay when the function h(p) is S-shaped. For example, consider the following series-parallel network and associated function:

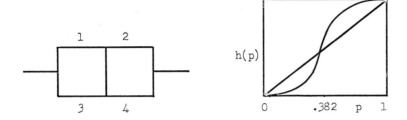

Note that the associated function

$$h(p) = \{1 - (1-p^2)\}^2 = 4p^2 - 4p^3 + p^4$$

does have the S-shape, with $h(p) < p$ for $p < .382$ and $h(p) > p$ for $p > .382$. Thus if the probability of failure of a relay to open when commanded to open is $< .382$ while the probability of failure of a relay to close when commanded to close is $< .618$, the series-parallel network will represent an improvement over a single relay.

The basic S-shape result for the function $h(p)$ of two-terminal networks may be stated as follows:

Theorem (Moore-Shannon) Let $h(p)$ be the probability of circuit closure for a two-terminal network, with $h(p) \neq p$. If for $0 < p_0 < 1$, $h(p_0) = p_0$, then $h(p) < p$ for $0 < p < p_0$, while $h(p) > p$ for $p_0 < p < 1$.

This means that for any two-terminal network the function $h(p)$ crosses the diagonal line of slope 1 at most once in the interval $(0, 1)$, the crossing occurring from below.

The proof depends on first solving the differential inequality

$$\frac{h'(p)}{h(p)\{1 - h(p)\}} > \frac{1}{p(1-p)} \quad \text{for } 0 < p < 1 . \tag{3.4}$$

The theorem then follows since one solution of the corresponding equality

$$\frac{h'(p)}{h(p)\{1 - h(p)\}} = \frac{1}{p(1-p)}$$

is $h(p) = p$. That is, the inequality (3.4) implies that at a point at which the curve $h(p)$ crosses the diagonal p, the function $h(p)$ must have greater slope, limiting the number of crossings to one at most.

Still pursuing their goal of arbitrarily high relay circuit reliability starting with arbitrarily crummy individual relays, Moore and Shannon next consider network 1 "composed" of elements each of which is a copy of network 2. It is clear that the resulting structure has function

$h_1[h_2(p)]$. If the process is iterated successively using the same
network function $h(p)$, the resulting function is $h\{h[h...h(p)...]\}$.
Graphical examination (verified by analytical proof) shows readily
that such a process of repeated composition for a function $h(p)$ which
crosses the diagonal at p_0 leads to a step function for

$$\lim_{n \to \infty} h^{(n)}(p) ,$$

since ordinates to the left of p_0 approach 0, ordinates to the right
of p_0 approach 1, while $h^{(n)}(p_0)$ remains equal to p_0 for each value
of n . Finally, starting with a so-called "hammock" network whose
$h(p)$ function does cross the diagonal once, and composing repeatedly,
Moore and Shannon explicitly obtain networks of arbitrarily high reliability. The Moore-Shannon papers represent an important step forward
in redundancy, containing a number of original ideas as well as a
good deal of ingenious analysis.

   Birnbaum, Esary and Saunders show in [6] that the Moore-Shannon
S-shape result holds for the larger class of coherent structures defined
above. Esary and Proschan [9] obtain more refined results relating
the crossings of $h(p)$ with curves of the form

$$\frac{h(p)}{1 - h(p)} = \frac{cp}{1-p} , \quad c > 0 ,$$

as a function of the number of minimal
paths of size 1 and the number of minimal cuts of size 1.

   In [9], a generalization of the inequality (3.4) is obtained for
coherent systems of components of differing reliabilities, $p_1, p_2, \ldots, p_n$.
The generalization states:

$$\sum_{i=1}^{n} p_i(1-p_i) \frac{\partial h(p)}{\partial p_i} \geq h(\underline{p})\{1 - h(\underline{p})\}, \tag{3.5}$$

where, as before, $\underline{p} = (p_1, p_2, \ldots, p_n)$. Inequality (3.5) provides
the basis for the following limited extension of the S-shape property
to coherent systems of unlike components.

   Theorem [9]. Let $p_i(\theta)$ satisfy for $i = 1, 2, \ldots, n$,

$$\frac{p_i'(\theta)}{p_i(\theta)\{1-p_i(\theta)\}} > \frac{1}{\theta(1-\theta)} , \quad 0 < \theta < 1 , \tag{3.6}$$

and let $h(\underline{p})$ be the reliability function of a coherent structure.
Then

$$[h(1-h)]^{-1} \frac{dh(\underline{p}(\theta))}{d\theta} > \frac{1}{\theta(1-\theta)} , \quad 0 < \theta < 1 . \tag{3.7}$$

Eq.(3.7) implies that h($\underline{p}(\theta)$) crosses the diagonal θ at most once.

The theorem states that the differential inequality (3.5) is preserved under composition. As an example of the application of the theorem, suppose that each component reliability is a function of a common parameter θ, the fraction of total effort expended on reliability improvement thus far. Suppose further that each $p_i(\theta)$ satisfies (3.6). Then the theorem tells us that system reliability is an S-shaped function of fractional effort expended.

REFERENCES

1. R. E. Barlow and L. C. Hunter, "Criteria for determining optimum redundancy," IRE Transactions on Reliability and Quality Control, April 1960.

2. R. E. Barlow and L. C. Hunter, "Mathematical models for system reliability, Part II," The Sylvania Technologist, Vol. XIII, No. 2, pp. 55-65, April 1960.

3. R. E. Barlow, L. C. Hunter, and F. Proschan, "Optimum redundancy when components are subject to open and short circuit failures," Boeing Scientific Research Laboratories Document D1-82-0093, March 1962.

4. R. E. Barlow, L. C. Hunter, and F. Proschan, "Probabilistic Models in Reliability Theorey," to be published by John Wiley and Sons.

5. R. Bellman and S. Dreyfus, "Dynamic programming and the reliability of multicomponent devices," Operations Research, Vol. 6, No. 2, pp. 200-206, March-April 1958.

6. Z. W. Birnbaum, J. D. Esary, and S. C. Saunders, "Multicomponent Systems and Structures and Their Reliability," Technometrics, Vol. 3, No. 1, February 1961.

7. G. Black and F. Proschan, "On Optimal Redundancy," Operations Research, Vol. 7, No. 5, pp. 581-588, September-October 1959.

8. C. J. Creveling, "Increasing the Reliability of Electronic Equipment by the Use of Redundant Circuits," Proceedings of the IRE, pp. 509-515, 1956.

9. J. D. Esary and F. Proschan, "The reliability of coherent systems," appearing in "Redundancy Techniques for Computing Systems," edited by Wilcox and Mann, Spartan Books, 1962.

10. B. J. Flehinger, "Reliability Improvement Through Redundancy at Various System Levels," IBM Journal of Research and Development,

Vol. 2, No. 2, pp. 148-158, April 1958.

11.   Robert Gordon, "Optimum Component Redundancy for Maximum System Reliability," Operations Research, Vol. 5, No. 2, April 1957.

12.   J. D. Kettelle, Jr., "Least-cost allocation of reliability investment," Operations Research, Vol. 10, No. 2, March-April 1962, pp. 249-265.

13.   H. Mine, "Reliability of Physical System," Transactions of the 1959 International Symposium on Circuit and Information Theory, May 1959.

14.   E. F. Moore and C. E. Shannon, "Reliable circuits using less reliable relays," Journal of the Franklin Institute, Vol. 262, Part 1, pp. 191-208, September 1956, and Vol. 262, Part II, pp. 281-297, October 1956.

15.   D. F. Morrison and H. A. David, "The life distribution and reliability of a system with spare components," Annals of Mathematical Statistics, Vol. 31, No. 4, December 1960.

16.   F. Moskowitz and J. B. McLean, "Some Reliability Aspects of System Design," IRE Transactions on Reliability and Quality Control, PGRQC-8, pp. 7-35, September 1956.

17.   F. Proschan, "Maximum reliability subject to linear constraints on redundancy," Boeing Scientific Research Laboratories Document, in preparation.

18.   F. Proschan, "Optimal System Supply," Naval Research Logistics Quarterly, Vol. 7, No. 4, pp. 609-646, December 1961.

19.   J. Von Neumann, "Probabilistic Logics," in Automata Studies, edited by C. E. Shannon and J. McCarthy, Princeton University, 1956.

DISCUSSION OF THE PAPER BY DR. PROSCHAN

G. P. Steck. One would hope, or perhaps even expect, that a
Kettelle-type algorithm would also exist for the multiple constraint
problem. The K-algorithm for the single constraint case represents
a dynamic programming approach in which the optimum property of a
multiple stage system is also possessed by the sub stages. For example, something like the following might work:

Consider constraints: $\quad s_j = \sum_{i=1}^{k} \gamma_{ij} n_i \quad, \quad i = 1, 2, \ldots, r \quad,$

$$(\text{my} \ \gamma_{ij} = \frac{c_{ij}}{c_i}) ;$$

the original problem is to maximize R subject to the condition that
$\max_i s_i \le 1$. Let the inverse problem be: given R to minimize $\max_i s_i$.
Then in two of the stages make a Kettelle-type table and a path through
it such that the next step is to the box which, out of all those with
larger R (smaller Q) , has the smallest $\max_i s_i$. Then put two of
these pairs of stages together in the same fashion, ..., etc. One then
gets a graph (hopefully nondecreasing) and R_0 would be the maximum R possible subject to constraint $\max_i s_i \le 1$.

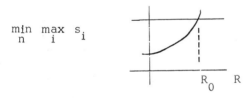

$$\min_{n} \ \max_{i} \ s_i$$

While I am afraid this procedure won't work in all cases, it may work
in some cases; and in any event should give a useful approximation
to the desired answer.

R. E. Barlow. The really serious drawback in my opinion to these
results is that the failure distribution must be known in order to compute the "optimal" solution. How do the results vary with different
distributions? Compare the uniform and exponential for example.

Gene B. Parrish. Can the optimization problem associated with
(1.1) and (1.2) be handled if (1.2) is replaced by an equation such
that the c_{ij} are dependent on n_i ? I am thinking in particular of the

typical case wherein the cost per item decreases with the number of items purchased.

Joseph B. Keller. When a system can fail in two or more ways, the different kinds of failure generally have different significance. Consequently it does not seem reasonable to weight them equally in defining the system reliability. Instead one might introduce the cost c_i of failure of type i and minimize the expected loss $\Sigma_i p_i c_i$ where p_i is the probability of failure of type i. In addition one may take into account the different amounts of time during which each type of failure can occur.

Israel Rotkin. What follows is not really a discussion of the paper, but a statement of two related problems suggested by the paper.

1. When several identical units are connected in parallel, so that at least one will do whatever needs to be done, they share the load while all are working. When one unit fails, the function is still performed, but in many cases the remaining units work harder to perform it. The life expectancy of the remaining units is reduced in these circumstances. As successive units fail, the strain on the remainder increases and the probability that they will fail does too. Similar statements can be made about identical units connected in series to guarantee that some function will be interrupted by at least one of them. An analysis of redundancy that took into account the increasing probability of failure of the remaining units as a result of the failure of some units would be very useful.

2. In many cases units are not connected directly in series or parallel, but the connection is made through a different kind of unit with characteristics of its own. For example, alternative power supplies may be connected to an operating room lighting system through a relay. Normally the lights are powered by the local utility company, but should that fail, the relay transfers the lights to a local standby power source.

In another kind of situation, several like units are interconnected through a different device, so all the first units work simultaneously; but the different device effectively disconnects any of the first kind of unit that fails in order to prevent destructive interaction.

Redundancy achieved through auxiliary devices as described above is sufficiently common to deserve special attention. This is an invitation to the statistical and mathematical fraternity to give it such attention.

Nathan Mantel. Dr. Proschan indicated a dominating sequence of steps which zigged and zagged across the plane. This sequence would tend to fall along a diagonal line. It might be worthwhile to follow the diagonal line only, checking the zigs and zags only at the

terminal portion. Where there are several constraints one could consider the convex envelope of diagonal lines.

With the above approach, one need not be restricted to consider
only two steps at a time. Instead they could all be considered simultaneously, particularly in the single constraint case. Starting from
any set of n_i's one would follow a steepest ascent procedure—the
particular n_i to be increased would be the one which produces the
greatest increase in reliability per unit cost. Close to the desired
degree of reliability one would start exploring alternative directions
of movement. I do not expect that pathologies would result from use
of steepest ascent procedures in this problem. It may be that it will
yield near-optimal rather than optimal solutions. In the multiple constraint problem, this may not work too readily.

Dr. Proschan replied at the seminar and later submitted the following in writing:

Dr. Proschan. The suggestion made by Dr. Steck is an interesting one. However, in some cases the multiple constraint problem re-
fuses to be reduced to the version suggested; i.e., the problem poser
will insist that he wants to maximize system reliability while not exceeding the cost, weight, volume, etc., available.

With regard to Dr. Barlow's point, often sample observations are available from which an empirical distribution may
be determined and used in place of the unknown true distribution. To
compare results assuming uniform and exponential distributions, see
Tables 1 and 2 of reference 3.

In reply to Mr. Parrish's question, in (1.2) the $c_{ij}n_i$ can be
replaced by $c_{ij}(n_i)$ provided the expression

$$\ln R(\underline{n}) + \lambda [c - \sum_{i=1}^{k} c_{ij}(n_i)]$$

remains concave. This would correspond, for example, to the case
where the cost per item increases with the number of items. (Note:
Dr. Keller mentioned a case where the cost per item would increase
with the number of items.) In the case of a single constraint a stronger
statement can be made. If for $i = 1, 2, \ldots, k$,

$$\frac{\ln(1 - q_i^{n+1}) - \ln(1 - q_i^n)}{c_i(n+1) - c_i(n)}$$

is a decreasing function of n, then the same sort of analysis as presented in the paper applies. Note that some cases of decreasing cost
per item are covered, although not all.

The variation of the model suggested by Professor Keller would certainly be of both practical and theoretical interest.

I would like to refer Mr. Rotkin to the following two references.
1. "A statistical model for life-length of material" by Z. W. Birnbaum and S. C. Saunders, Journal of the American Statistical Association, March 1958, Vol. 53, pp. 151-160, does specifically assume that after component failure, the strain on the remaining components increases. However, it does not attempt to determine optimum redundancy, but simply to provide a probability distribution for system life.

2. "Reliability improvement through redundancy at various system levels" by B. J. Fehinger, IBM Journal of Research and Development, Vol. 2, No. 2, April 1958, allows for the unreliability of a failure-detecting device and of a switching device as well as that of the operating components. The aim is to determine the optimum level at which redundancy should be applied.

However, it is true that most mathematicians find it more convenient to ignore the unreliability of auxiliary devices such as failure detectors or switches. An honest treatment of the complete, more realistic model would be refreshing though quite difficult.

Nathan Mantel's suggestion is a good one and should result in a decrease in the time required to compute the solution using the Kettelle algorithm.

RICHARD E. BARLOW
Maintenance and replacement policies

1. INTRODUCTION

This is a modest attempt to describe some of the models and results relevant to replacement problems. The selection of material has
been governed by the author's own interests as well as by an attempt
to treat only a few of the practical problems of more general interest.

In many situations, failure of a unit during actual operation is
costly or dangerous. If the unit is characterized by a failure rate
that increases with age, it is wise to replace it before it has aged
too greatly. On the other hand, one cannot plan too frequent replacements without incurring excessive costs. Thus, one of the most important replacement problems is that of specifying a replacement
policy which balances the cost of failures against the cost of planned
replacements.

For example, suppose that a unit which is to operate continuously
over some time period $(0, t)$ is replaced upon failure. If a replacement policy is in effect, replacement of the unit may occur before
failure. Suppose a cost c_1 that includes all costs resulting from a
failure and its replacement is incurred for each failed item that is replaced. A cost $c_2 < c_1$, that again includes all costs is incurred
for each non-failed item that is exchanged. If $N_1(t)$ denotes the
number of actual failures in $(0, t)$ and $N_2(t)$ denotes the number
of exchanges for non-failed items in $(0, t)$, $(N_1(t)$ and $N_2(t)$ being
random variables), then the expected cost $C(t)$ during $(0, t)$ is

$$C(t) = c_1 E[N_1(t)] + c_2 E[N_2(t)]$$

where E denotes expected value. We will assume later for this particular model that the usage period extends into the indefinite future
and try to minimize the stationary expected cost per unit time, i.e.,

$$C^* = \lim_{t \to \infty} \frac{C(t)}{t} .$$

A strictly periodic policy is in force if we always replace an item exactly at the time of failure or s hours after its installation, which- ever occurs first; s is a constant. A random periodic policy differs only in that s is a random variable. A sequentially determined re- placement policy is one in which the replacement interval is determined at each removal in accordance with the time remaining to the time span.

In a series of reports [13, 14, 15], G. H. Weiss considered the effects on system reliability and on maintenance costs of both strictly periodic and random periodic replacement policies for an essentially infinite usage period. The operating characteristics of random peri- odic policies were determined by Flehinger [7]. A theory of optimum sequential replacement policies for the case of a finite time horizon was developed by Barlow and Proschan in [4].

One of the earliest treatments of the replacement problem was made by A. J. Lotka in 1939 [9]. Campbell, in a paper appearing in 1941 [5], discussed the comparative advantages of replacing a num- ber of street lamps either all at once or as they failed. Clearly the cost per lamp of replacing all lamps at once is much less than the cost of replacing each lamp as it fails. The cost of the additional lamps required for preventive maintenance must be balanced against the cost of the additional failures that occur if replacement is post- poned.

A common variant of the replacement problem is to consider the time for replacement as non-negligible. In this circumstance we seek a policy which maximizes expected operating time. Let c_1 denote the expected time to replace a failed component and c_2 denote the expected time to replace a non-failed component $(c_1 \geq c_2)$. This problem has been treated by Morse [10] and Barlow and Hunter [1] among others. Let E_T denote the expected fractional amount of time the item is operating in $(0, t)$ and

$$E_\infty = \lim_{T \to \infty} E_T .$$

It is easy to show (e.g., [1], p. 97) that

$$C^* = \frac{1}{E_\infty} - 1 .$$

Hence any replacement policy which minimizes C^* , maximizes E_∞ and the solution to the replacement problem is also the solution to the second problem when c_1 and c_2 are properly identified.

In so-called preparedness models [12], failure may only be de- tected by an inspection. For example, a piece of equipment may be kept in storage for use in case of emergency. The objective of deci- sions taken is to maintain the equipment in a state of operational readiness. The distinctive feature of preparedness models is that the actual state of the equipment at any time can be ascertained only by

inspection. If the equipment is found to have failed, repair or replacement follows inspection. Radner and Jorgenson [11] obtain optimum
replacement schedules for simple models.

2. FAILURE DISTRIBUTIONS WITH INCREASING HAZARD RATE

Optimal replacement policies are only optimal with respect to a
given failure distribution, say F. In practice we may know little or
nothing about F. Hence it seems more reasonable to look for policies which are "good" on the basis of only limited information concerning F. We may, for example, have some knowledge of the mean
and variance or perhaps a percentile of F. In addition, we may suppose that the items considered are wearing out with time.

Define

$$F_x(t) = \frac{F(t+x) - F(x)}{1 - F(x)}$$

for $t \geq 0$. Then $F_x(t)$ is a distribution in $t \geq 0$ and is the probability of failure in $(x, x+t)$ given survival to age x. If F has a
density f, then the hazard rate is usually defined as

$$q(t) = f(t)/[1 - F(t)] \quad .$$

Using the well-known relation

$$1 - F(t) = \exp[-\int_0^t q(x)\,dx]$$

is easily seen that $F_x(t)$ increasing in x for all $t \geq 0$ is equivalent
to the assertion that the hazard rate is increasing in t.

If $F_x(t)$ is non-increasing in x, then no replacement should be
considered. This follows since the conditional failure distribution is
"improving" with age. Hence replacement before failure would result
in replacing an aged component by a "worse" component.

Since most materials, structures and devices for which replacement is considered wear out with time, the class of distributions for
which the hazard rate is increasing (i.e., non-decreasing) is one of
special interest. Ignoring the possibility of "infant" mortality, this
is perhaps the strongest, most natural assumption that can be made
for failure distributions.

The properties of distributions with a monotone hazard rate have
been studied by Barlow, Marshall and Proschan [3]. Chebyshev type
bounds for this class of distributions have been determined by Barlow
and Marshall in [2]. The important properties of distributions with increasing hazard rate follow from the concavity of $\log[1 - F(t)]$.* Clearly
$f(t)/[1 - F(t)]$ is increasing if and only if the second derivative of
$\log[1 - F(t)]$ is non-positive. For convenience we denote distributions

---

*
Functions with this property are also called Pólya frequency functions
of order 2 and have been studied by I. J. Schoenberg, e.g. J. d'Analyse
Math., Vol. I (1951), pp. 331-374.

for which $\log[1 - F(t)]$ is concave by IHR (for increasing hazard rate). It follows easily from the log concavity that

$$[1 - F(t)]^{1/t}$$

is decreasing in t when F is IHR and $F(0) = 0$. In particular, if a percentile such as the median, say M, is known and F is IHR, then

$$[1 - F(t)] \geq 2^{-t/M}$$

for $t \leq M$. The inequality is of course reversed for $t > M$. Since the exponential distribution with constant hazard rate is the boundary distribution between distributions with increasing hazard rate and those with decreasing hazard rate, it provides natural Chebyshev type bounds on $1 - F(t)$. In particular, if F is IHR and $\mu_r = \int_0^\infty t^r dF(t)$ $(r \geq 1)$, then

$$1 - F(t) \geq \begin{cases} \exp[-t/\sqrt[r]{\lambda_r} & \text{for } t < \sqrt[r]{\mu_r} \\ \\ 0 & \text{elsewhere} \end{cases} \tag{2.1}$$

where $\lambda_r = \mu_r/\Gamma(r+1)$. This result is proved in [2] where it is extended. If F is IHR, then

$$1 - F(t) \leq 1 - x_0 \quad \text{for } t \geq \mu_1 \tag{2.2}$$

where x_0 satisfies

$$1 - x_0 = \exp[-x_0 t/\mu_1].$$

The bound is tabulated in Table I. Sharper bounds are known in terms of higher moments, [2]. Table II tabulates upper bounds on $1 - F(t)$ in terms of the first moment ($\mu_1 = 1$) and the second moment μ_2. More accurate and extensive tables are in preparation. Bounds on the p-th percentile in terms of the mean can also be obtained. For example, if M is the median,

$$(\log 2)\mu_1 \leq M \leq (2 \log 2)\mu_1. \tag{2.3}$$

All of the above bounds are sharp. Their proofs and extensions appear in [2]. We will apply these bounds in evaluating replacement policies in the next section.

If F is IHR, then the moments of F have important properties. For one,

$$\log \left(\frac{\mu_i}{i!} \right) \qquad (2.4)$$

is a concave sequence in $i = 0, 1, 2, \ldots$ where

$$\mu_i = \int_0^\infty x^i dF(x) \ .$$

From this it follows easily that

$$(\lambda_i)^{1/i}$$

is decreasing in i where $\lambda_i = \mu_i/i!$. In fact, (2.4) is strictly decreasing except for the exponential distribution. From (2.4) we obtain the well-known result for IHR distributions that

$$\sigma/\mu_1 \leq 1$$

where σ is the standard deviation.

3. EVALUATION OF REPLACEMENT POLICIES

A strictly periodic replacement policy is in force if we always replace an item at the time of failure or τ hours after its installation, whichever occurs first; τ is considered fixed. We confine attention to strictly periodic replacement policies since they are perhaps the most practical.

3.1. Replacement Policies for a Single Unit

The probability that an item will not fail while in service before time t is

$$\bar{S}_\tau(t) = [1 - F(\tau)]^n [1 - F(t-n\tau)] \qquad (3.1)$$

where F is the failure distribution of the item and $n\tau \leq t \leq (n+1)\tau$. Note that $S_\tau(t)$ is a distribution function if we define

$$\bar{S}_\tau(t) = 1 - S_\tau(t) \ .$$

Assume that F has a density. Differentiating $\bar{S}_\tau(t)$ with respect to τ , we see that

$$\bar{S}_{\tau_1}(t) \geq \bar{S}_{\tau_2}(t) \qquad (3.2)$$

for all $\tau_1 \leq \tau_2$ if and only if F is IHR. In particular, if F is IHR,

$$\bar{S}_\tau(t) \geq 1 - F(t) \ . \qquad (3.3)$$

This indicates that strictly periodic replacement is always beneficial when F is IHR. Of course, this is not true if F has decreasing hazard rate.

Weiss [13] obtained the n-th moments, $M_n(\tau)$ for the distribution of time to failure in service. In particular, the first moment, $M_1(\tau)$, is easily calculated from (3.1), to be

$$M_1(\tau) = \frac{\int_0^\tau \bar{F}(x)\, dx}{F(t)}$$

where $\bar{F} = 1 - F$.

If F is IHR, then it follows from (3.2) that

$$\frac{\int_0^{\tau_1} \bar{F}(x)\, dx}{F(\tau_1)} \geq \frac{\int_0^{\tau_2} \bar{F}(x)\, dx}{F(\tau_2)}$$

for $\tau_1 < \tau_2$. As we would expect for IHR distributions, the more often we schedule replacement, the longer the mean time to an in-service failure.

Upper bounds on $M_1(\tau)$ in terms of two moments can be obtained using Table II. Since $\bar{S}_\tau(t) \geq 1 - F(t)$ we know of course

$$M_1(\tau) \geq \mu_1 \qquad (3.4)$$

for IHR distributions. Using the fact that $[1 - F(t)]^{1/t}$ is decreasing in t, sharper lower bounds on $M_1(\tau)$ are available in terms of percentiles. For example, if $\tau \leq$ Median, then

$$M_1(\tau) \geq \frac{\text{Median}}{\log 2} \geq \mu_1 \qquad (3.5)$$

using (2.3). If we agree to replace at time

$$\tau \leq \mu_1$$

then

$$\bar{S}_\tau(t) \geq \exp[-t/\mu_1] \qquad (3.6)$$

for all t. This is an immediate consequence of (2.1).

Under the same restrictions we obtain

P[Number of in-service failures in $(0, t) \geq n$]   (3.7)

$$\leq \sum_{j=n}^\infty \frac{[t/\mu_1]^j}{j!} \exp[-t/\mu_1]$$

for all t . The exponential distribution and the related Poisson process thus provide conservative estimates of the probability that an item will not fail in service before time t and the probability of n or more in-service failures in $(0, t)$.

Again, assuming $\tau \leq \mu_1$ and using the result that $F(x)$ is dominated from above by the distribution

$$G(x) = \begin{cases} 1 - e^{-x/\mu_1} & x < \tau \\ 1 & x \geq \tau \end{cases}$$

when F is IHR we obtain bounds on the number of removals for both failed and non-failed items. In particular,

$$P[n \text{ or more removals in } (0, t)] \leq R(n, t)$$

where

$$R(n, t) = \int_0^t e^{-x} \frac{x^{n-1}}{(n-1)!} \, dx \tag{3.8}$$

$$+ \sum_{j=1}^{\min(k-1, n)} \binom{n}{j} e^{-t} \sum_{m=0}^{j-1} (-1)^m \binom{j-1}{m} \frac{(t-j\tau)^{n+m-j}}{(n-j+m)!}$$

for $(k-1)\tau \leq t < k\tau$, $k = 1, 2, \ldots$. The expected number of removals in $(0, t)$ is bounded above by $E_R(t)$ where

$$E_R(t) = \frac{1}{(1-e^{-\tau})^2} \{ t - (t+\tau-1) e^{-\tau} - e^{-2\tau} - (t+1-k\tau) e^{-k\tau}$$

$$+ [t+1-(k-1)\tau] e^{-(k+1)\tau} \} \tag{3.9}$$

for $(k-1)\tau \leq t \leq k\tau$. These quantities were computed in an article by Hunter and Proschan [8] for another purpose.

3.2 Block Replacement

Under a policy of block replacement all components of a given type are replaced simultaneously at times independent of the failure history of the system. These policies have been investigated by Welker [16], Drenick [6] and Flehinger [7]. They are perhaps more realistic since they do not require the keeping of records on component use.

Consider a network consisting of n units in parallel and suppose a policy of block replacement is followed every τ hours. The probability that the network will not fail in service before time t is

$$\bar{S}_\tau(t) = \{1 - F(\tau)]^n\}^k \{1 - [F(t-k\tau)]^n\}$$

for $k\tau \leq t < (k+1)\tau$. If the failure distribution is IHR and $\tau \leq \mu_1$, then using (2.1)

$$\bar{S}_\tau(t) \geq \{1 - [1 - \exp(-\tau/\mu_1)]^n\}^k \{1 - [1 - \exp(-\frac{t-k\tau}{\mu_1})]^n\}$$

for $(k-1)\tau \leq t < k\tau$. The moments of the distribution of the time be-tween actual network failures were computed by Weiss [13] for expo-nential failure and now are recognized as lower bounds for replacement intervals $\tau \leq \mu_1$. In particular, the mean time between actual net-work failures $M_1(\ )$, satisfies

$$M_1(\tau) \geq \mu_1 B_n [1 - \exp(-\frac{\tau}{\mu_1})] / [1 - \exp(-\frac{\tau}{\mu_1})]^n$$

where the functions $B_n(x)$ are

$$B_n(x) = x + \frac{x^2}{2} + \frac{x^3}{3} + \ldots + \frac{x^n}{n} .$$

3.3 Optimum Replacement Intervals

Again suppose that single items are replaced on the basis of age and let c_1 denote the cost suffered for each failed item which is re-placed. A cost $c_2 < c_1$ is suffered for each non-failed item which is exchanged. Again this includes all costs. The optimum replace-ment policy for this model was treated by Barlow and Proschan [4] for the cases of a finite and infinite time horizon. The finite time horizon is appropriate for items which become obsolescent.

Let $E[N_1(\tau)]$ and $E[N_2(\tau)]$ denote the expected number of failures and the expected number of exchanges respectively per unit time if we replace a component either at time τ or at failure which-ever occurs first. Then the expected cost per unit time (stationary expected cost), $C(\tau)$, is

$$C(\tau) = c_1 E[N_1(\tau)] + c_2 E[N_2(\tau)]$$

$$= \frac{c_1 F(\tau)}{\int_0^\tau [1 - F(x)] \, dx} + \frac{c_2 \bar{F}(\tau)}{\int_0^\tau [1 - F(x)] \, dx} \tag{3.10}$$

Recall that we can also interpret c_1 as the mean time to replace a failed component and c_2 as the mean time to replace a non-failed component. Then $C(\tau)$ becomes the average down-time per unit time if we replace at time τ or at failure, whichever occurs first.

If we have no information concerning F , then the minimax replacement strategy is to never schedule replacement. It is perhaps somewhat surprising that this policy is also minimax if we know only the mean (μ_1) of F . To see this, let $L(\tau, F) = C(\tau)$ and $F_0(x) = 1 - e^{-x/\mu_1}$. Then

$$\frac{c_1}{\mu_1} = \max_F L(\infty, F) \geq \min_\tau \max_F L(\tau, F) \geq \max_F \min_\tau L(\tau, F)$$

$$\geq \min_\tau L(\tau, F_0) = L(\infty, F_0) = \frac{c_1}{\mu_1} \quad .$$

Hence the minimax strategy is never to schedule replacement. It can be shown that this policy is minimax even when μ_1 and μ_2 are given, provided

$$[2 - \frac{c_2}{c_1}](\mu_1)^2 \leq \mu_2 \leq 2(\mu_1)^2 \quad .$$

In general, however, a knowledge of the second moment as well as the mean is required in order to determine an optimal finite replacement interval.

Differentiating $C(\tau)$ with respect to τ , we see that the optimum policy τ_0 for specified F satisfies

$$q(\tau_0) \int_0^{\tau_0} [1 - F(x)] dx - F(\tau_0) = \frac{c_2}{c_1 - c_2} \quad . \tag{3.11}$$

If F is IHR, there is always a unique optimum policy (possibly infinite). This can be verified by differentiating (3.11) and using the definition of IHR distributions. In general, the cost curve will look like Figure 1. The dotted line is the expected cost per unit time under a policy of replacement at failure only.

Since $1 - F(\tau) \leq 1$, $C(\tau) \geq c_2/\tau$ and the optimum replacement interval, τ_0 , will always satisfy

$$\tau_0 \geq \frac{c_2}{c_1} \mu_1 \quad ,$$

when F is IHR . Hence we should never consider replacing more frequently than

$$\frac{c_2}{c_1} \mu_1 \quad .$$

Using Table II, we can determine a function $U(t) \geq 1 - F(t)$ depending on μ_1 and μ_2 such that

$$C(\tau) \geq \frac{c_2 + (c_1 - c_2)[1 - U(\tau)]}{\int_0^\tau U(x)\,dx} \quad .$$

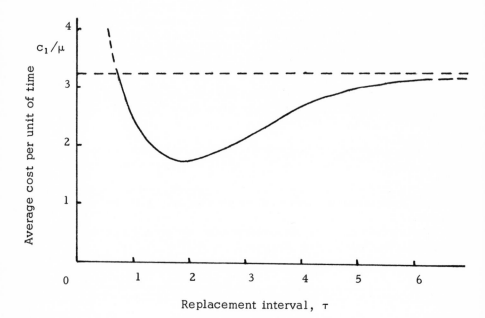

Figure 1

Setting the right-hand side equal to c_1/μ_1 , we can determine τ^* such that

$$\tau_0 \geq \tau^*$$

always holds. This lower bound on τ_0 is of course far from optimum. Using lower bounds on $1 - F(t)$ we can determine upper bounds on $C(\tau)$ and in this way evaluate competing policies. Upper bounds on $C(\tau)$ can be obtained in terms of percentiles. For example, if we replace at time $\tau \leq M$ where M is the median of F , then

$$C(\tau) \leq (c_1 - c_2)\,\frac{\log 2}{M} + \frac{c_2 \log 2}{M[1 - 2^{-\tau/M}]} \quad .$$

3.4 Preparedness Models

Recall that for preparedness models, failure may only be detected by an inspection. The objective is to maintain the equipment in a state of operational readiness.

The following simple model was treated by Radner and Jorgenson [11]. Let τ denote the time between replacement. The equipment is replaced after time τ whether or not it has failed by that time. Let K denote the average time to perform a replacement. Since replacement serves as a regeneration point of the process, the optimal policy is strictly periodic, and it suffices to maximize operating time over a single cycle. The average time the equipment is operating over a cycle is

$$A(\tau) = \frac{\int_0^\tau \bar{F}(x)\, dx}{\tau + K} \ .$$

Using Tables I and II we can obtain a bound $U(x)$ such that

$$1 - F(x) \leq U(x) \ .$$

From (2.1) we have a bound $L(x)$ such that

$$1 - F(x) \geq L(x) \ .$$

Hence we have bounds on $A(\tau)$, namely

$$\frac{\int_0^\tau L(x)\, dx}{\tau + K} \leq A(\tau) \leq \frac{\int_0^\tau U(x)\, dx}{\tau + K}$$

which can be used in evaluating competing replacement policies.

Differentiating $A(\tau)$ with respect to τ, it can be shown that the optimal τ_0 satisfies

$$\varphi(\tau) = (\tau + K)\bar{F}(\tau) - \int_0^\tau \bar{F}(x)\, dx = 0 \ .$$

It can be shown that for any failure distribution F there is only one solution and it maximizes $A(\tau)$. Using the bounds on $\bar{F}(\tau)$, bounds on the optimum replacement interval τ_0 can be obtained.

REFERENCES

1. Barlow, R., and L. Hunter. Optimum Preventive Maintenance Policies, Operations Research, 1960, 8(1), 90-100.

2. Barlow, R. and A. Marshall. Chebyshev Type Inequalities for Distributions with Monotone Hazard Rate. (To appear.)

3. Barlow, R., A. Marshall, and F. Proschan. Properties of Probability Distributions with Monotone Hazard Rate. Boeing Scientific Research Lab. Scientific Note. No. 247, Jan. 1962.

4. Barlow, R., and F. Proschan. Planned Replacement. Studies in Applied Prob. and Management Science, (Arrow, Karlin, and Scarf, editors), Stanford University Press, Stanford, Calif., 1962.

5. Campbell, N. R. The Replacement of Perishable Members of a Continually Operating System, J. Roy. Stat. Soc., 1941, 7 (suppl.), 110-30.

6. Drenick, R. F. Mathematical Aspects of the Reliability Problem, J. Soc. for Indust. and Appl. Math., 1960, 8(1), 125-49.

7. Flehinger, B. J. A General Model for the Reliability Analysis of Systems Under Various Preventive Maintenance Policies, Annals of Math. Stat., 1962, 33(1), 137-56.

8. Hunter, L. and F. Proschan. Replacement When Constant Failure Rate Precedes Wearout. Naval Res. Logist. Quart., 1961, 8(2), 127-36.

9. Lotka, A. J. A Contribution to the Theory of Self-Renewing Aggregates with Special Reference to Industrial Replacement, Annals of Math. Stat., 1939, 10(1), 1-25.

10. Morse, P. M. Queues, Inventories, and Maintenance, New York: Wiley, 1958.

11. Radner, R. and D. W. Jorgenson. Optimal Replacement and Inspection of Stochastically Failing Equipment (same as ref. 4).

12. Savage, I. R. Cycling, Naval Res. Logistic. Quart., 1956, 3(3), 163-75.

13. Weiss, G. H. On the Theory of Replacement of Machinery with a Random Failure Time, Naval Res. Logist. Quart., 1956, 3(4), 279-94.

14. Weiss, G. H. On Some Economic Factors Influencing a Reliability Program, NAVORD Report 4256, U. S. Naval Ordnance Lab., White Oak, Md.

15. Weiss, G. H.   The Reliability of a Redundant System Which Op-
     erates Repitively, NAVORD Report 4348, U. S. Naval Ordnance
     Lab., White Oak, Md.

16. Welker, E. L. (1959).   Relationship between Equipment Reliability,
     Preventive Maintenance Policy, and Operating Costs, Proc. Fifth
     Nat'l. Symp. on Rel. and Qual. Control, 270-80.

TABLE I

UPPER BOUNDS ON 1 - F(t)

$$(F \text{ is IHR}, \quad \mu_1 = \int_0^\infty t \, dF(t) = 1)$$

t	IHR Bound	Markov Bound (1/t)	t	IHR Bound	Markov Bound (1/t)
1. 0	1. 0	1. 0			
1. 1	0. 820	0. 909	3. 1	0. 053	0. 323
1. 2	0. 687	0. 833	3. 2	0. 047	0. 313
1. 3	0. 577	0. 769	3. 3	0. 042	0. 303
1. 4	0. 488	0. 714	3. 4	0. 038	0. 294
1. 5	0. 416	0. 667	3. 5	0. 034	0. 286
1. 6	0. 358	0. 625	3. 6	0. 030	0. 278
1. 7	0. 308	0. 588	3. 7	0. 027	0. 270
1. 8	0. 268	0. 555	3. 8	0. 024	0. 263
1. 9	0. 233	0. 526	3. 9	0. 022	0. 256
2. 0	0. 203	0. 500	4. 0	0. 020	0. 250
2. 1	0. 178	0. 476	4. 1	0. 018	0. 244
2. 2	0. 156	0. 455	4. 2	0. 016	0. 238
2. 3	0. 138	0. 435	4. 3	0. 014	0. 233
2. 4	0. 121	0. 417	4. 4	0. 013	0. 227
2. 5	0. 107	0. 400	4. 5	0. 012	0. 222
2. 6	0. 095	0. 385	4. 6	0. 011	0. 217
2. 7	0. 084	0. 370	4. 7	0. 010	0. 213
2. 8	0. 075	0. 357	4. 8	0. 009	0. 208
2. 9	0. 067	0. 345	4. 9	0. 008	0. 204
3. 0	0. 059	0. 333	5. 0	0. 007	0. 200

Maintenance and Replacement Policies

TABLE II

UPPER BOUNDS ON $1 - F(t)$

$$(F \text{ is IHR, } \mu_1 = \int_0^\infty t\,dF(t) = 1, \; \mu_2 = \int_0^\infty t^2\,dF(t))$$

t \ μ_2	1.1	1.2	1.3	1.4	1.5	1.6	1.7	1.8	1.9	2.0
0.1	1.000	1.000	1.000	1.000	1.000	1.000	1.000	1.000	0.952	0.905
0.2	1.000	1.000	1.000	1.000	1.000	1.000	0.964	0.910	0.862	0.819
0.3	1.000	1.000	1.000	1.000	0.993	0.929	0.873	0.824	0.780	0.741
0.4	1.000	1.000	1.000	0.969	0.901	0.841	0.790	0.746	0.706	0.670
0.5	1.000	1.000	0.956	0.880	0.817	0.763	0.716	0.675	0.639	0.607
0.6	1.000	0.959	0.871	0.800	0.741	0.691	0.648	0.611	0.578	0.549
0.7	0.987	0.877	0.794	0.727	0.672	0.626	0.587	0.553	0.523	0.497
0.8	0.914	0.805	0.724	0.661	0.610	0.567	0.531	0.500	0.473	0.449
0.9	0.850	0.740	0.661	0.601	0.554	0.514	0.481	0.453	0.428	0.407
1.0	0.796	0.682	0.605	0.548	0.503	0.466	0.436	0.410	0.387	0.368
1.1	0.756	0.632	0.554	0.499	0.456	0.423	0.395	0.371	0.351	0.333
1.2	0.634	0.589	0.509	0.455	0.415	0.383	0.357	0.336	0.317	0.301
1.3	0.411	0.554	0.469	0.415	0.377	0.348	0.324	0.304	0.287	0.273
1.4	0.258	0.444	0.434	0.380	0.343	0.315	0.293	0.275	0.260	0.247
1.5	0.163	0.321	0.404	0.349	0.312	0.286	0.266	0.249	0.235	0.223
1.6	0.104	0.231	0.332	0.321	0.285	0.260	0.241	0.225	0.213	0.202
1.7	0.068	0.167	0.254	0.296	0.260	0.236	0.218	0.204	0.193	0.183
1.8	0.045	0.121	0.194	0.258	0.238	0.215	0.198	0.185	0.174	0.165
1.9	0.030	0.089	0.149	0.205	0.218	0.195	0.179	0.167	0.158	0.150
2.0	0.021	0.066	0.115	0.163	0.200	0.178	0.163	0.152	0.143	0.135
2.1	0.014	0.049	0.089	0.130	0.169	0.162	0.148	0.137	0.129	0.122
2.2	0.010	0.037	0.070	0.104	0.138	0.148	0.134	0.124	0.117	0.111
2.3	0.007	0.028	0.055	0.084	0.113	0.135	0.122	0.113	0.106	0.100
2.4	0.005	0.022	0.044	0.068	0.093	0.118	0.110	0.102	0.096	0.091
2.5	0.004	0.017	0.035	0.055	0.077	0.099	0.100	0.092	0.087	0.082
2.6	0.003	0.013	0.028	0.045	0.064	0.083	0.091	0.084	0.078	0.074
2.7	0.002	0.010	0.022	0.037	0.053	0.070	0.083	0.076	0.071	0.067
2.8	0.001	0.008	0.018	0.030	0.044	0.059	0.074	0.069	0.064	0.061
2.9	0.001	0.006	0.014	0.025	0.037	0.050	0.063	0.062	0.058	0.055
3.0	0.001	0.005	0.012	0.021	0.031	0.042	0.054	0.057	0.053	0.050
3.1	0.000	0.004	0.010	0.017	0.026	0.036	0.046	0.051	0.048	0.045
3.2	0.000	0.003	0.008	0.014	0.022	0.031	0.040	0.047	0.043	0.041
3.3	0.000	0.002	0.006	0.012	0.019	0.026	0.034	0.042	0.039	0.037
3.4	0.000	0.002	0.005	0.010	0.016	0.022	0.030	0.037	0.035	0.033
3.5	0.000	0.001	0.004	0.008	0.013	0.019	0.026	0.032	0.032	0.030

DISCUSSION OF THE PAPER BY DR. BARLOW

J. D. Esary. I would like to state a mild reservation about the class of IHR distributions as the basis for the non-parametric procedures that we would all like to see in reliability. Since the "components" treated in a problem may very well be assemblies of other "components," it seems that an appropriate requirement on the class of distributions considered is that it be closed under the formation of reasonable systems. Series assemblies of IHR components have the IHR property, but examples exist of redundant assemblies of IHR components which do not have this property.

H. Leon Harter. First, a comment on Dr. Esary's remark: If a component has IHR, then two such components in parallel have IHR. Even if the individual component has constant hazard rate, two in parallel will have IHR. (It is assumed that the situation is one in which the combination of two components in parallel functions if either component functions; that is, that the failure mode behaves like an open circuit, not like a short circuit.)

Second, a question to the speaker: Suppose a system contains a large number of components of the same type. One naive replacement policy would be to replace all components of a given type whenever one of them fails. Has any study been made of the properties of such a policy?

Frank Proschan. Dr. Barlow has pointed out that in most practical problems we do not know the failure distribution of the unit whose maintenance we are considering. Therefore he suggests that we use bounds obtained from a knowledge of the mean or second moment or possibly both, under the assumption of an IHR distribution.

I submit that in those situations in which we do not know the underlying failure distribution, we also do not know the moments. What usually is available is a sample of observations; if such is the case then it would be preferable, I believe, to use the empirical distribution to deduce optimum replacement intervals or replacement policy operating characteristics, rather than to estimate the mean or second moment and then obtain bounds based on these. The empirical distribution simply provides more information than does the sample mean or second moment.

Actually, I propose that in the many practical situations where knowledge of the failure distribution is incomplete, the replacement policy should be a sequential statistical one. By that I mean that after each failure or planned replacement, all the information available

up to that time should be used to determine the next replacement interval. The criterion for arriving at each of these replacement intervals
should be minimum total expected cost over the time period of interest
(or minimum total expected cost per unit of time if the period is
infinite).

   K. Zenkere. We have just completed a rather elaborate system
study on wave guides. Our sole price of information was that 26 were
tested for 1,000 hours with one failure. Using this information, we were
able to use Barlow's work to obtain a satisfactory maintenance plan.
The one thing I would like to stress is that these optimum intervals
are far from critical. There is a lot of "slop." Even if one knew the
optimum policy, one would find from practical reasons that actual replacements may range from 1/2 to double the intended interval without
too much effect on the optimizing function.

   M. Zelen. 1. Frank Proschan's remarks mark the first time that
the use of prior information has arisen in this seminar. However,
when Dick Barlow is using the idea of an increasing hazard rate, he
also is making use of prior information. The prior information may
take several forms. It may be earlier observations on the same system or one might have a new system and the prior information may be
the "feeling" of the technician or scientist who has had experience
with similar systems. He might have prior information which one
would like to incorporate into any initial planned policy. I feel this
is the direction in which we must go in order to obtain the "realistic"
planned replacement policies which Frank Proschan mentioned.
   2. Dick Barlow's work should be very useful when one is working with the quantiles of a distribution. As Ken Zenkere mentioned,
he tested twenty-six items for a thousand hours with only one failure.
Here one has very good information on a quantile, but rather unsatis-
factory information with respect to the mean-time-to-failure. Actually the "tradition" of using the mean-time-to-failure is a satisfactory
measure of performance only when the failure distribution is exponential. I have always advocated using quantiles as a measure of performance. Speaking to engineers, one often finds that the mean-time-
to-failure is interpreted as median-time-to-failure. It seems to me
that if specifications were set in terms of quantiles, then all of
Dick's work also works for the median-time-to-failure (or any other
quantile) and should be very useful in the acceptance sampling
situation. However, I don't think Dick's work would be too useful
in situations where items are supposed to operate a very long time,
i.e., extreme quantiles. His bounds are useful in the interval of
performance from (say) t = 0 to the mean.

   Nathan Mantel. I would suggest considering the average (or,

following up on Zelen's suggestion, median) remaining lifetime function, as well as the hazard function. This function may give additional insight into optimal replacement times and policies. I suspect that
Barlow's results may apply to survival functions with decreasing
average remaining lifetime. This class of survival functions includes
and is wider than the class of functions with increasing hazard rate.
Barlow's results would thus be increased in generality.

Israel Rotkin. It may be of some interest to a group of statisticians to know how non-statisticians solved a maintenance and replacement problem intuitively.

During World War II, I was a radar officer on an amphibious command ship in the central Pacific. The air-search radar on my ship was
more powerful than any other in our group, and its antenna was significantly higher than that of the others. Therefore it was very important
that my radar function properly, especially during action or when action was imminent.

My radar had a transmitter with four output tubes so connected
that all were required to work properly to insure proper working of the
radar, and these tubes were the weakest link by far in the whole equipment. Early in the war these tubes had an expected lifetime of about
one hundred hours, but strenuous efforts were being made to extend
this lifetime, and, in fact, each successive lot of tubes I acquired
did have a longer average lifetime.

The captain of my ship and the admiral of the fleet both resisted
strenuously all attempts to shut down this radar set when it was operable, because then they were dependent upon radars with lesser
capabilities. However, the same authorities insisted that the chance
of failure of the radar during action be vanishingly small.

I solved the problem as follows: During periods of comparative
safety, I would let the radar run until it failed (usually because a
transmitter tube failed). Then I would replace only the part that had
failed in order to restore operation. I kept accurate records of the
working life of each part that failed. When action was imminent or
during periods of action, I replaced parts (usually only transmitter
tubes) according to the life history built up during the preceding
period of calm and on a conservative basis. In this way my radar
was always working when it mattered most. In addition, my operating
time between replacements increased as the tubes improved.

In comparing notes with other radar officers charged with similar
responsibilities, I discovered later that this was a fairly common
procedure.

Henry Ellner. In maintaining supplies subject to chemical deterioration, care and preservation or overhauling can be performed at
stated intervals. It seems that the deterioration or degradation of

components and sub-assemblies are comparable to failure distributions
with increasing hazard rate. The question is whether the replacement
policy discussed in the paper is appropriate for material with shelf-
lives reflecting increasing "hazard" rates. Apparently, a preparedness
model may furnish a suitable analogy for supplies or equipment inspected periodically to ascertain their serviceability or state of readiness.

    Dr. Barlow replied at the seminar and later submitted the follow-
ing in writing:

    R. Barlow. Dr. Esary has raised a good point and I find his ex-
ample interesting. However, as Dr. Esary is aware, the IHR property
is preserved under convolution and, furthermore, the order statistics
from a sample of an IHR random variable again have this property.
To seek a natural, relatively small family of distributions closed under
very many additional restrictions is perhaps asking too much.
    As a counterexample to L. Harter's assertion consider a system
of two parallel components with failure distributions

$$F_1(t) = 1 - e^{-2t}$$

$$F_2(t) = 1 - e^{-t} .$$

Then the failure rate of the system is

$$q(t) = \frac{e^{-t}[1 + 2e^{-t} - 3e^{-2t}]}{e^{-t}[1 + e^{-t} - e^{-2t}]}$$

Note that $q(0) = 0$, $q(+\infty) = 1$ and $q(\log 3) = 12/11$. The failure
rate increases and then decreases.
    The class of distributions mentioned by Mr. Mantel are of course
exactly those distributions F for which

$$\log \int_t^\infty [1 - F(x)]\,dx$$

is concave in t . It is still true for this class that $\left\{ \dfrac{\mu_i}{i!} \right\}_{i=0}^\infty$
(the normalized moment sequence) is log concave and hence the co-
efficient of variation $\sigma/\mu_1 \leq 1$. Also $f(0) \leq 1/\mu_1$. The Chebyshev
type inequalities mentioned in my paper do not seem to follow. However, different bounds can be obtained. This more general class of
distributions deserves more attention. It would be interesting to
discover whether or not this property is preserved under convolution,
for example.
    Mr. Ellner's problem seems to fall under the heading of prepared-
ness models as discussed in my paper.

Dr. Zelen has answered very well some of the objections raised by Frank Proschan. To use the empirical distribution alone, as Proschan suggests, to deduce optimum replacement intervals would mean ignoring valuable prior information in many situations. The IHR assumption, when it is justified, provides a great deal of information about the nature of the failure distribution.

Mr. Rotkin's practical solution to the replacement problem is very interesting. However, I gather that the only deterent to frequent replacement was the supply of spares available. In this case the problem deserving mathematical treatment would be to determine the size of the spare parts kit. The use of accumulated failure history to modify the replacement needs further consideration as several people have pointed out.

Commenting on Dr. Zelen's discussion, I should like to mention that life test sampling tables have been constructed by Prof. Shanti Gupta using the IHR upper bound on survival probability mentioned in my paper. These tables will appear in a Stanford University Technical Report entitled, "Non-Parametric Life Test Sampling Plans." More extensive tables providing bounds on probability distributions with monotone hazard rate are being prepared by the General Telephone and Electronics Laboratories.

The discussion by Mr. Zenkere was most interesting. He informs me that a paper discussing applications of the IHR bounds will soon appear.

LARRY C. HUNTER
Optimum checking procedures

The problem of checking or inspection arises in connection with
systems which are deteriorating. Deterioration is stochastic and the
condition of the system is known only if it is inspected. The optimization problem is to minimize the total expected costs of the lapsed
time between system failure and detection of failure, and the costs of
checking. For military systems, the costs of an undetected failure are
often interpreted as lost readiness time with a consequent reduction
in the operational availability of the system. For consumer goods,
there are costs for keeping a unit which has failed or for delivering a
defective item. For a production system, this cost is often measured
by defective items produced.

For example, consider the problem of detecting the arrival of an
object whose arrival time is unknown. Each inspection involves a
cost so that we do not wish to check too often. On the other hand,
there is a penalty cost associated with the lapsed time between arrival and detection of the arrival.

Many different checking models of varying complexity have been
treated in the literature. All models take into account, in some manner, the costs of checking and of undetected failure. Some include
the possibility of failure during checking and of imperfect inspection
where a failure is detected only with probability p . Two types of
errors are often considered, namely, the probability of calling a good
system bad or a bad system good. Often the check is considered to
induce a stress on the system and hence increase the likeliness of
system failure. Each of these variations can be applied to checking
policies where checks are regularly scheduled every fixed period of
time T , or to policies in which the times between checks are not
equal but depend on the time and information gained during the last
check.

No pretense is made for complete coverage of the literature on the
various models of the checking problem. However, it is hoped that by
dividing the subject into two parts, a fair insight into this important
problem can be obtained. The first part of this division will discuss

95

optimum checking procedures with general failure distributions. As
should be expected, the similar and less complicated models are analyzed in this general setting. The second part considers more complicated models under the assumption of exponential failure.

1. CHECKING PROCEDURES WITH GENERAL FAILURE DISTRIBUTIONS

The failure distribution will be denoted by $F(t)$, i.e., $F(t)$ is
the probability of system failure by time t . In order to specify a
checking procedure, it is sufficient to specify a sequence of random
variables $\{X_k\}$, called the inter-checking times, which may be degenerate. If the random variables are identically distributed, the associated checking procedure is called <u>periodic</u>. If the random variables
are not identically distributed, the checking procedure is called <u>se-
quential</u>. In the latter case, the intervals between checks usually depend upon $F(t)$ and hence upon the time the system has been in
operation. The class of sequential checking procedures of course includes the class of periodic checking procedures. We shall first discuss this more general class of policies and then consider the less
general but more widely applied periodic policies.

1.1 Sequential Checking Procedures

In 1956, Savage [1] treated a general model in which he supposed
that it is desired to check a set of elements at time $\{x_i\}$ with a fixed
cost of inspecting or replacing these elements. He assumes that there
is a function $L(T)$ which denotes the loss incurred if the time between
two successive checks is T . When $L(T)$ is a non-decreasing, con-
tinuous function with $L(0) = 0$, and such that $\frac{L(T)}{T} \to \infty$ as $T \to \infty$,
Savage shows that the total cost assumes its minimum value.

By restricting the loss function we shall be able to say a great
deal more about the nature of optimum solutions. In the remainder of
this section, we assume that (a) system failure is known only through
checking and that checking detects a failure with probability one,
(b) checking does not degrade the system, and (c) the system cannot fail while being checked. There are two costs involved: (1) each
check entails a fixed cost c_1 , (2) the time elapsed between system
failure and its discovery at the next check results in a cost of c_2 per
unit of time. The problem considered is to specify a sequence of check
times which will minimize the expected total costs. c_1 and c_2 can
be generalized costs measured in money, time, or any other relevant
penalty. In circumstances where it is desirable to minimize the total
expected system down-time, c_1 would denote the time to perform a
check and $c_2 = 1$.

Let $\{X_n\}$ be a sequence of random variables denoting the inter-
checking times; let $N(t)$ denote the number of checks in $(0, t)$; and
$\gamma(t)$, the time to discovery if the system fails at time t . Then the

loss is

$$c_1 [N(t) + 1] + c_2 \gamma(t)$$

if the system fails at time t, since it must be checked once more before the failure is discovered. For a given system failure distribution F, the expected loss is

$$E[\text{Loss}] = \int_0^\infty \{c_1 [M(t) + 1] + c_2 E[\gamma(t)]\} dF(t) \qquad (1)$$

where $M(t) = E[N(t)]$ is the familiar renewal quantity of renewal theory when the checking procedure is periodic. Any checking procedure which minimizes this objective function will be called an optimum checking procedure.

This checking problem as it is formulated here was first introduced in "Mathematical Models for System Reliability" [2]. The general solution which we shall now give is summarized in [3] and contained in total in [4]. In [5] analogous policies were considered for items which are replaced until a finite time horizon is reached.

The first thing to note is that it is fairly easy to show that any random sequential checking policy can be improved upon by a non-random sequential policy [5]. Hence an optimum policy will be defined by an increasing sequence of non-negative numbers $\{x_k\}_{k=0}^\infty$. The k-th check is performed at time x_k if the system has not failed by the (k-1)-th check. Note that if the system fails at time t where

$$x_k \le t \le x_{k+1}$$

the cost incurred is

$$c_1(k+1) + c_2(x_{k+1} - t) \quad .$$

Hence the expected loss is

$$E[\text{Loss}] = \sum_{k=0}^\infty \int_{x_k}^{x_{k+1}} [c_1(k+1) + c_2(x_{k+1} - t)] dF(t) \qquad (2)$$

When $F(x)$ is a continuous failure distribution with finite mean μ, then there exists an optimum degenerate checking procedure and the inter-checking times can be explicitly formulated.

Theorem 1. If $F(x)$ is continuous with finite mean μ, there exists an optimum degenerate checking procedure.

Because of the general iterative procedure used to determine the optimum checking times we shall briefly sketch a proof of this theorem.

For any increasing sequence of non-negative numbers $\{x_k\}$ define $E_k = [x_k, x_{k+1}]$. Let $S = \{t \mid F(t) < 1\}$ and let $\bar{S}$ be the closure of S. Define

$$L(x) = \inf_{\substack{0 < x_1 < x_2 \dots \\ U_k E_k \supset \bar{S}}} \sum_{k=0}^{\infty} \int_{x_k}^{x_{k+1}} \{c_1(k+1) + c_2(x_{k+1}-t)\} \frac{dF(t+x)}{\bar{F}(x)}$$

where $\bar{F}(x) = 1 - F(x)$ and $x_0 = 0$. Thus $L(x)$ is the infimum of remaining expected cost over all policies given that the component has
not yet failed at age x. The first step in the proof is to establish
that $L(x)$ is a bounded, continuous function of x. The optimum
check policy $\{x_k^*\}$ may then be defined in the following manner. Let
x_1 be the smallest value of x which minimizes

$$c_1 + \int_0^x c_2(x-t)\,dF(t) + L(x)\bar{F}(x) .$$

In a similar fashion let x_i be the smallest value minimizing

$$c_1 + \int_0^x c_2(x-t) \frac{dF(x_{i-1}^* + t)}{\bar{F}(x_{i-1}^*)} + L(x_{i-1}^* + x) \frac{\bar{F}(x_{i-1}^* + x)}{\bar{F}(x_{i-1}^*)}$$

where $x_i^* = x_1 + x_2 + \dots + x_i$, for $i = 1, 2, \dots$. Then $\{x_k^*\}$ is
the optimum degenerate checking procedure.

It should be noted that our model requires a scheduled check at
time T in cases where it is known that the system will fail within a
given interval $[0, T]$. This convention is for convenience in the proof
of Theorem 1. The following theorem gives necessary and sufficient
conditions on the failure distribution to ensure that we need only
check at the end of the interval.

Theorem 2. Let $F(t) = 1$ for $t \geq T$. If

$$F(t) \leq \frac{1}{1 + \frac{c_2}{c_1}(T-t)}$$

for $0 \leq t \leq T$, then the optimum checking policy will consist of a
single check performed at time T. Conversely, if

$$F(t) > \frac{1}{1 + \frac{c_2}{c_1}(T-t)}$$

for some $0 \leq t \leq T$, then the optimum checking policy will require, in
addition to the check at time T, one or more checks before time T.

Proof: If a single check is performed at time T, the expected cost is

$$c_1 + c_2 \int_0^T (T-t)\, dF(t) = c_1 + c_2 \int_0^T F(t)\, dt \ .$$

If an additional check is performed at time x, the expected cost is

$$\int_0^x \{c_1 + c_2(x-t)\}\, dF(t) + \int_x^T \{2c_1 + c_2(T-t)\}\, dF(t)$$

$$= c_1 + c_1\{1-F(x)\} + c_2 \int_0^T F(t)\, dt - c_2(T-x)\, F(x) \ .$$

Thus a single check at time T is preferable if

$$c_1\{1 - F(x)\} - c_2(T-x)\, F(x) \geq 0 \qquad \text{for } 0 \leq x \leq T$$

or

$$F(x) \leq \frac{1}{1 + \dfrac{c_2}{c_1}(T-x)} \qquad \text{for } 0 \leq x \leq T \ .$$

Moreover, this implies that a single check at time T is preferable to a single check at time T preceded by two checks at, say, times x_1 and x_2. Given that a check has occurred at time x_1, a single check before T, namely at time x_2, is warranted if and only if

$$\frac{F(x_2) - F(x_1)}{\bar{F}(x_1)} > \frac{1}{1 + \dfrac{c_2}{c_1}[(T-x_1) - (x_2-x_1)]} \ .$$

But the above inequality implies

$$F(x_2) > \frac{1}{1 + \dfrac{c_2}{c_1}(T - x_2)}$$

since

$$F(x_2) > \frac{F(x_2) - F(x_1)}{\bar{F}(x_1)}$$

This contradicts our assumption that

$$F(x) \leq \frac{1}{1 + \dfrac{c_2}{c_1}(T-x)} \qquad \text{for } 0 \leq x \leq T \ .$$

Similarly it is easy to see that this assumption implies that a single check at time T is preferable to n checks before time T.

Conversely, if for some x in $(0, T)$ the assumption is not true, then checks at times x and T yield lower expected cost than does a

single check at time T. Thus the optimum checking policy will require
in addition to the check at time T, one or more checks before time T.

An explicit recursion formula can be given for computing the optimum checking sequence when the failure rate of the system is increasing, that is, the system tends to wear out from the moment it is put
into use. Actually, although we feel that the assumption of increasing
hazard (failure) rate should be sufficient, to date we must require a
stronger condition. Namely, we assume that the failure density f is
a Pólya frequency function of order $2(PF_2)$, i.e., that $\frac{f(x-a)}{f(x)}$ is
non-decreasing in x for any $a > 0$. This restriction implies that the
failure rate is increasing (the converse does not hold) and is satisfied by a large class of distributions including the normal, the gamma

$$\frac{\lambda^\alpha x^{\alpha-1} e^{-\lambda x}}{\Gamma(\alpha)} \qquad \text{for } \alpha \geq 1$$

and the Weibull

$$\lambda\beta x^{\beta-1} e^{-\lambda x^\beta} \qquad \text{for } \beta \geq 1 .$$

Since an optimum policy exists by Theorem 1, a necessary condition that a sequence $\{x_k\}$ be a minimum cost checking procedure
is that

$$\frac{\partial E[\text{Loss}]}{\partial x_k} = 0$$

for all k. Hence, using (2) we obtain

$$x_{k+1} - x_k = \frac{F(x_k) - F(x_{k-1})}{f(x_k)} - \frac{c_1}{c_2} \qquad (3)$$

Note that this sequence is determined recursively once we choose x_1.
We shall now show how to choose x_1^* and hence determine the optimum check times $\{x_k^*\}$.

Theorem 3. If the failure density f is PF_2 and $f(x) > 0$ for $x > 0$,
then the times between successive checks are non-increasing.

The proof of this theorem depends heavily on properties of Pólya
frequency functions and will not be given here.

To see that the optimum checking times do not in general occur
more and more frequently, consider the following example.

Example. Suppose that an item will fail with probability p at time
1 or with probability $1-p$ at time 3. Alternatively, we can imagine a
density approximating such a two-spiked probability distribution.
Theorem 2 implies that it pays to check at times 1 and 3 if

$$p > \frac{c_1}{c_1 + 2c_2} \quad .$$

The interval between checking times increases rather than decreases in this case. However, the failure distribution does not have the properties of a Pólya frequency function.

Theorem 4 below gives us a powerful tool for computing optimum checking procedures when f is a Pólya frequency function. We shall use the following notation. If $\{x_n\}$ is an increasing sequence, $\Delta_n = x_{n+1} - x_n$, $n = 0, 1, 2, \ldots$ where $\Delta_0 = x_1$; $\{x_n^*\}$ denotes, as before, an optimal checking sequence.

<u>Theorem 4.</u> Let f be a Pólya frequency function of order 2, $f(t) > 0$ for $t > 0$, and not of the form ae^{bt} over any open interval. Choose $x_1 > 0$ and determine $\{x_k\}$ recursively by

$$x_{k+1} - x_k = \frac{F(x_k) - F(x_{k-1})}{f(x_k)} - \frac{c_1}{c_2} \quad .$$

If $x_1 > x_1^*$, $\Delta_n > \Delta_{n-1}$ for some positive integer n .

If $x_1 < x_1^*$, $\Delta_n < 0$ for some positive integer n .

Thus for this wide class of functions a computing procedure for determining the optimum sequence is first to choose a value for x_1 . A good first guess would be to choose x_1 so that

$$c_1 = c_2 \int_0^{x_1} (x_1 - t)\, dF(t) = c_2 \int_0^{x_1} F(t)\, dt \quad .$$

The cost of a single check is thus balanced against the expected cost of undetected failure occurring before the first check.

Next compute the x_k's recursively using (3). If any $\Delta_k > \Delta_{k-1}$, reduce x_1 and repeat; if any $\Delta_k < 0$, increase x_1 and repeat. The following example involving the normal distribution illustrates the ease of obtaining bounds on the unique solution.

<u>Example.</u> Suppose the time to failure is approximately normally distributed with mean $\mu = 500$ hours and standard deviation $\sigma = 100$. Suppose furthermore that $c_1 = 10$ and $c_2 = 1$. Then for the first check at times $x_1 = 422.4$ hours and $x_1 = 422.5$ hours, we have the following computed times for additional checks.

k	x_k	Δ_k	k	x_k	Δ_k
1	422. 50	64. 29	1	422. 40	64. 20
2	486. 79	.	2	486. 60	.
.	.	.	.	.	.
.	.	.	.	.	.
.	.	.	.	.	.
8	.	27. 48	13	.	10. 50
9	727. 81	27. 40	14	815. 98	1. 00
10	755. 21	30. 00	15	816. 98	-9. 00
11	785. 21		16	807. 98	

Hence $x_1 = 422.5$ is too large since $\Delta_{10} > \Delta_9$ and $x_1 = 422.4$ is a little too small since $\Delta_{15} < 0$. The proper time to schedule the first check is between 422.4 hours and 422.5 hours.

Example. Suppose the time to failure of a system is uniformly distributed over the interval $(0, T)$. Then

$$E[\text{Loss}] = \sum_{k=0}^{\infty} \int_{x_k}^{x_{k+1}} [c_1(k+1) + c_2(x_{k+1} - t)] \frac{dt}{T} \quad .$$

By Theorem 1 and equation (3) we know an optimum solution exists and satisfies

$$x_{k+1} - x_k + \frac{c_1}{c_2} = x_k - x_{k-1} \quad .$$

Solving for x_k in terms of x_1, we have

$$x_k = kx_1 - \frac{k(k-1)}{2} \frac{c_1}{c_2} \quad .$$

Hence $x_1 > \frac{k-1}{2} \frac{c_1}{c_2}$ for all k which implies that we only make a finite number of checks, say n.

Since we require $x_n = T$, we find that

$$x_k = \frac{kT}{n} + k(n-k)\frac{c_1}{2c_2} \quad (k = 0, 1, \ldots, n) \quad . \tag{4}$$

$\{x_k\}$ defines a valid checking sequence when $x_{k+1} - x_k > 0$ for all k or when

$$\frac{T}{n} + \frac{c_1}{2c_2}(n - 2k - 1) > 0 \text{ for all } k$$

$$\therefore n(n-1) < \frac{2c_2 T}{c_1} \quad .$$

On the other hand, if we compare the expected loss of making $n+1$
and n checks we have, by direct computation, that

$$L(n+1) - L(n) = -\frac{2c_2}{T} \frac{n+1}{n}(\frac{T}{n+1} - \frac{c_1 n}{2c_2})^2 < 0 .$$

Therefore the $\{x_k\}$ are given by (4) where n is the largest integer
such that $n(n-1) < 2c_2/c_1$.

When the time to failure is uniformly distributed over the interval
$[0, 100]$ and each check costs 2 units, the optimum number of checks
is $n = 10$. ($c_1 = 2$, $c_2 = 1$.) The times these checks should be made
are from (4) at 19, 36, 51, 64, 75, 84, 91, 96, 99, and 100 hours.

Derman [6] gave a minimax solution for the loss function (2) of
this section. For this analysis one assumes no knowledge concerning the distribution function of the life of the unit. The aim is to
derive the schedule which minimizes the maximum possible expected
cost associated with the inspections and failures of the unit. Assuming that a failure is detected with probability p , the optimal checking
schedule is given by

$$x_i = ip\left[\frac{T}{np+1} + \frac{c_1}{2c_2}\left\{\frac{n[p(n+1)+2]}{np+1} - (i+1)\right\}\right] \quad i = 0, 1, \ldots, n$$

where n is the largest integer such that

$$c_1 p^2 n + c_1 p(2-p) n + 2(c_1 - pc_2 T) \leq 0 .$$

This answer is the same as that derived in the previous example for the
uniform failure distribution when $p = 1$. The apparent discrepancy in
answers stems from the fact that Derman does not allow a check at time T

1.2. Periodic Checking Procedures

Although the class of periodic checking procedures is optimum
over the class of all checking procedures only for the case of exponential failure, this procedure is the most commonly applied. A great
many papers have been written on optimum periodic checking and we
shall now attempt to summarize some of these results.

B. J. Flehinger [7] considers two interesting problems under the
heading of system check-outs and marginal testing. In the first of
these a component may fail while it is not being used but it will not
introduce a system failure until it is called into use once more. The
periods of use and non-use follow different exponential distributions.
Under marginal testing it is assumed that a component is in one of
three states σ A(good), B(marginal), or C(failed). In state A, a component operates satisfactorily in the system and passes the marginal
test if it is performed. In state B , it operates satisfactorily but fails

the test if it is performed. In state C, it does not perform its function in the system and fails the test if it can be performed. For each of these problems Flehinger derives integral equations for

$A(x: y)$ = probability that the component is preventively removed by time x

$B(x: y)$ = probability a component introduces a system failure by time x

$C(x: y)$ = probability a component is removed by time x

where each quantity is conditioned by the fact that the component entered the system at time y . Both x and y are measured from the time of the last preventive removal.

Another model of marginal checking was considered by R. F. Drenick [8]. He considered a discrete version of this problem by assuming that the failures can only occur at the end of a check period. A device is to be checked in multiples of the check period and preventively replaced at age n if the measured parameter x is greater than a failure threshold x_1 . The device fails at that time if it was below x_1 at age $n-1$ but above at age n . Drenick gives renewal equations for the probability of failure at time n and the probability of preventive replacement at that time.

In our discussion of optimal periodic policies we shall begin with the simple model considered in the last section. As before, c_1 will denote the cost of a check and c_2 the cost per unit of an undetected failure. If we check periodically every x time units, our expected loss is

$$E[\text{Loss}] = \sum_{k=0}^{\infty} \int_{kx}^{(k+1)x} \{(k+1)c_1 + c_2[(k+1)x - t]\} dF(t) .$$

When the failure distribution is exponential, $F(t) = 1 - e^{-\lambda t}$,

$$E[\text{Loss}] = \frac{c_1 + c_2 x}{1 - e^{-\lambda x}} - \frac{c_2}{\lambda} . \tag{5}$$

This convex function has a unique minimum when x satisfies

$$e^{\lambda x} - \lambda x = 1 + \lambda \frac{c_1}{c_2} \tag{6}$$

When the time to failure is uniformly distributed between $[0, T]$

$$E[\text{Loss}] = \frac{c_1(n+1)}{2} + \frac{c_2 T}{2n} .$$

This expression is minimized when n is chosen to be the largest

integer such that $n(n-1) \leq c_2 T/c_1$. Recall that for the optimum sequential checking policy n was the largest integer such that
$n(n-1) \leq 2c_2 T/c_1$. Thus, for the uniform distribution, the ratio of
the number of checks following an optimum sequential policy to an optimum periodic policy is approximately $\sqrt{2}$.

2. PERIODIC CHECKING PROCEDURES WHEN THE FAILURE DISTRIBUTION IS EXPONENTIAL

The exponential is, by far, the most commonly assumed failure
distribution. Historically, it has been found that many components
and systems experience exponential failures. D. J. Davis [9] has
found that this failure law characterizes a wide variety of devices including ball and roller bearings, vacuum tubes, passenger-bus motors,
and many other electronic systems. Drenick [10] shows that under
reasonably general conditions, the distribution of the time between
failure tends to the exponential as the complexity and the time of
operation increase.

In the remainder of this section we shall assume the failure distribution is $F(t) = 1 - e^{-\lambda t}$. The solution for the cost model of the
last section has already been derived for this distribution (eqs. (5)
and (6)). We shall therefore devote the remainder of the discussion
to the problem of maximizing a different objective function—system
availability.

Kamins [11] and Coleman and Abrams [12] have extensively
studied checkout procedures to maximize operational readiness. Each
considers the possibility that checking may subject the system to
further stresses that may lead to failure. The probabilities of calling
a good system bad and a bad system good are included in their analyses. In order to summarize the results of [12], we introduce the following additional notation:

T = checking period
q = probability of failure during checkout period
T_c = duration of a checkout period
p_c = probability of failure occurring before actual
test, if failure occurs during a checkout period
T_r = duration of replacement repair period
α = probability of calling a good system bad
β = probability of calling a bad system bad

The model considered is one in which the system is to be checked
for failure at periods of time T . The duration of the checkout period,
T_c , is not considered as system down-time when there is not a system failure. The assumptions of constant probability of failure, q ,
and constant probability of detection of a failure during test p_c , seem

somewhat unrealistic.   The time interval used in determining the availability is the expected time between successive checking and/or replacement periods.

$$\text{Availability} \ = \ \frac{\text{Expected up-time}}{\text{Expected interval length}}$$

$$= \frac{1 - e^{-\lambda T}}{\lambda(T+T_c)\beta^{-1}\{1+e^{-\lambda T}[q(1-\alpha+\alpha p_c - p_c \beta)-(1-\beta)]\} + \lambda T_r[1-(1-q)(1-\alpha)e^{-\lambda T}]}$$

The case of perfect checkout, i.e., the checkout test will always
detect a failed system and never make a false alarm, is found by setting $\alpha = 0$ and $\beta = 1$.

Kamins, in general, considers the same model with one important
exception.   Kamins uses the time between scheduled checks, T, in
determining system availability.   Hence repair and checking times sub-
tract directly from the up-time in the interval of length T.   Additional
differences are that a check imposes a stress (probability of failure)
q on a good system and that the system may fail during repair following the same exponential law.   Such a failure cannot be detected until
the next system check.   For this model the availability in the case of
perfect checkout when checking time is considered as down-time is

$$\text{Availability} \ = \ \frac{e^{-\lambda T_r}(e^{\lambda T}-1+q) - q + 1 - e^{\lambda T_c}}{\lambda T e^{\lambda T}} \ .$$

As a final comment it should be noted that one of the serious objections to the use of maximum readiness as the goal for checkout
scheduling is that it entirely ignores costs.   A more meaningful approach is to maximize

$$\frac{\text{Availability}}{\text{Total Cost}} \ .$$

Here the total cost should include the fixed, direct, and indirect costs
of checking.

REFERENCES

1. I. R. Savage, "Cycling," Naval Research Logistics Quarterly, Vol. 3, 1956, pp. 163-175.

2. R. Barlow and L. Hunter, "Mathematical Models for System Reliability," The Sylvania Technologist, Vol. XIII, No. 2, April 1960.

3. R. Barlow and L. Hunter, "Optimum Checking Procedures," Proc. Seventh Nat'l. Symp. on Rel. and Qual. Cont., No. 9, 73 (1960) or G. T. and E. Research and Dev. Jour., Vol. 1, No. 1, January 1961.

4. R. Barlow, L. Hunter, and F. Proschan, "Optimum Monitoring Procedures," Boeing Scientific Research Labs. Document D1-82-0104, April 1961.

5. R. Barlow and F. Proschan, "Planned Replacement," appearing in "Studies in Applied Probability and Management Science," edited by K. J. Arrow, S. Karlin, and H. Scarf, Stanford University Press, 1962.

6. C. Derman, "On Optimal Surveillance Schedules," Columbia Univ. Stat. Eng. Group, Tech. Rpt. No. 12, Nov. 1, 1960.

7. B. J. Flehinger, "A General Model for the Reliability Analysis of Systems Under Various Preventive Maintenance Policies," Annals of Math. Stat., 33(1), 1962, pp. 137-156.

8. R. F. Drenick, "Mathematical Aspects of the Reliability Problem," J. Soc. Indust. Appl. Math., Vol. 8, No. 1, 1960.

9. D. J. Davis, "On Analysis of Some Failure Data," J. Amer. Stat. Ass'n., Vol. 47, No. 258, June 1952.

10. R. F. Drenick, "The Failure Law of Complex Equipment," J. Soc. Indust. Appl. Math., Vol. 8, No. 4, Dec. 1960.

11. M. Kamins, "Determining Checkout Intervals for Systems Subject to Random Failures," Rand Research Memo. RM-2578, June 15, 1960.

12. J. Coleman and I. Abrams, "Mathematical Model for Operational Readiness," J. Operation Res. Soc., Vol. 10, No. 1, Jan.-Feb. 1962, pp. 126-139.

DISCUSSION OF THE PAPER BY DR. HUNTER

Betty J. Flehinger. This paper raises an exceedingly interesting problem and, given the objective function postulated, it provides a novel and ingenious method of finding the optimum sequence of check points.

However, for most practical situations, there is a serious question about the validity of the objective function, i.e., the costs associated with checking and with down time per system failure. Normally, when checking is planned, it is carried out so that repair or replacement may take place when failure is discovered. The system is needed for some period of time, and, during that period, we have a sequence of checks until failure is discovered, replacement, then another sequence of checks, and so on. The objective function to be minimized is then $C(t)$ the expected cost of checking, down time, and replacement for t, that period of time. If the system is to be used for some indefinite period of time, the objective function is the asymptotic expected cost per unit time, i.e.,

$$\lim_{t \to \infty} \frac{C(t)}{t} = \frac{L + c_3}{\mu_R}$$

where

$$L = \sum_{k=0}^{\infty} \int_{x_k}^{x_{k+1}} [c_1(k+1) + c_2(x_{k+1} - t)] dF(t) = \text{Hunter's objective function}$$

c_3 = Cost of replacement

μ_R = Expected time between replacements

$$= \sum_{k=0}^{\infty} x_{k+1}[F(x_{k+1}) - F(x_k)] .$$

A general minimization procedure for this function is not easy to find, but some general observations can be made and explicit results will be obtained for the case of exponential failure.

Note that a necessary condition for an optimum sequence of check points is:

$$\frac{\partial}{\partial x_k} \left[\lim_{t \to \infty} \frac{C(t)}{t} \right] = 0 .$$

109

Now

$$\frac{\partial}{\partial x_k}\left[\lim_{t\to\infty}\frac{C(t)}{t}\right] = \frac{\mu_R\frac{\partial L}{\partial x_k} - (L+c_3)[F(x_k)-F(x_{k-1})-(x_{k+1}-x_k)f(x_k)]}{\mu_R^2}$$

In Hunter's optimum sequence, we have

$$\frac{\partial L}{\partial x_k} = 0$$

and

$$F(x_k)-F(x_{k-1})-(x_{k+1}-x_k)f(x_k) = \frac{c_1}{c_2}f(x_k) \quad,$$

so that, at each of his check points,

$$\frac{\partial}{\partial x_k}\left[\lim_{t\to\infty}\frac{C(t)}{t}\right] = -\frac{(L+c_3)c_1 f(x_k)}{c_2\mu_R^2} \quad.$$

Since this derivative is negative, it follows that, given an optimal sequence as defined by Hunter, the asymptotic expected loss can be decreased by increasing the time of any check point. Surely, then, an optimum sequence from the long-time point of view, will have longer check intervals than does a Hunter sequence.

In order to gain insight into the order of magnitude of the difference between the two types of optimum sequences, consider the case of exponential failure. With either objective function, the optimum sequence is strictly periodic. As indicated in Eq. 6, Hunter's check interval x satisfies

$$e^{\lambda x} - \lambda x - 1 = \lambda\frac{c_1}{c_2} \tag{1}$$

which has a unique solution for all values of λ, c_1, and c_2.

On the other hand, for a check interval of length x, we have,

$$\lim_{t\to\infty}\frac{C(t)}{t} = \frac{1}{x}\left\{c_1 + c_2\int_0^x (x-y)\,dF(y) + c_3 F(x)\right\}$$

$$= \frac{c_1}{x} + c_2\left[1 - \frac{1}{\lambda x}(1-e^{-\lambda x})\right] + c_3\left(\frac{1-e^{-\lambda x}}{x}\right)$$

Differentiating with respect to x, we find that the optimal interval satisfies

$$\Gamma_2(\lambda x) = 1 - e^{-\lambda x}(1+\lambda x) = \frac{\lambda c_1}{c_2 - \lambda c_3} \quad. \tag{2}$$

This has a unique solution if $c_2 > \lambda(c_1 + c_3)$. If $c_2 \le \lambda(c_1 + c_3)$, the optimal policy is no checking.

The accompanying graph has the left sides of Eqs. 1 and 2 plotted against λx. Note that the right side of Eq. 2 is equal to or greater than the right side of Eq. 1, with equality corresponding to $c_3 = 0$. It is clear that the solution to Eq. 2 is always greater than the solution to Eq. 1. Suppose for example that $\lambda \frac{c_1}{c_2}$ is equal to .72, so that Eq. 1 gives $\lambda x = 1$. Then the solution to Eq. 2 will be $\lambda x \geq 2.5$. For $\frac{\lambda c_1}{c_2}$ close to 0 and c_3 close to 0, the two sequences will be nearly the same.

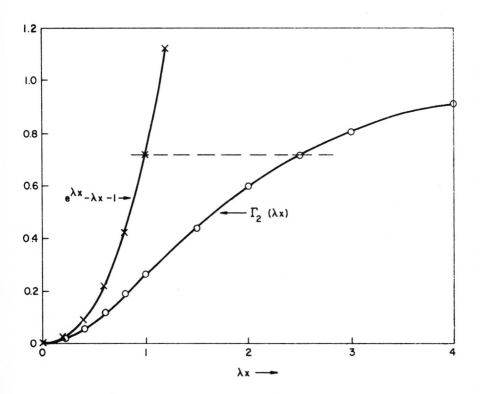

George Weiss. I have looked at the Hunter-Barlow-Proschan model when one allows a probability less than one that a check will discover a failed element. Unfortunately, a neat answer is not available in this case, although if the parameter β is close to one, a perturbation solution might be possible.

M. Zelen. I would like to remark, following Dick Barlow's line of reasoning when he was reviewing the literature, that everything depends on knowing the failure distribution. He made some remarks to the effect that one never really knows the failure distribution and then outlined how to obtain bounds on optimum scheduling by using information about moments or quantiles. It would seem that the same situation applies here. Also with respect to your recommendations on future work, I believe one might have a large amount of prior information about how the system is operating. This should be utilized in some way until one feels certain that a reasonably good monitoring system is in operation. The "optimum" monitoring system should evolve with experience with the system.

Dr. Hunter replied at the seminar and later submitted the following in writing:

Dr. Hunter The loss function, E[Loss], the total expected cost due to checking and undetected failure, is most applicable to those situations in which no further checking activity is contemplated once "failure" is detected. Consider, for example, the detection of an object, such as a radio signal, plane or missile, whose arrival time is unknown. "Failure" in this case, of course, means arrival. Another example is that of the investor who wishes to contact his stock broker as quickly as possible to place a sell order. From long experience he knows the broker's arrival distribution. The model of the paper would minimize the investor's total expected cost of time spent in, say, telephoning and the cost of lapsed time between the broker's arrival and the placement of the sell order. In addition, the objective function minimized in the paper is a reasonable one for systems which are to be used for some definite, finite time period. It is particularly suitable for study of systems in which repair or replacement is not possible, but where it is important to monitor the operating state of the system.

In those situations in which checking is followed by repair or replacement, and in which the system is to be used for some indefinite period of time, I believe the asymptotic expected cost per unit time as presented in Flehinger's comments is better although it is harder to work with. However, for any application, the model must be carefully and explicitly formulated for that specific application.

One can make a simple observation relating the asymptotic

expected cost per unit time and the objective function of the paper. In Dr. Flehinger's comments

$$\lim_{t \to \infty} \frac{C(t)}{t} = \frac{L + c_3}{\mu_R}$$

If μ_R is written as $\mu_R = \mu + \gamma$ where μ_R is the mean time to failure and γ is the mean interval between failure and detection, then it is apparent that minimizing $\lim_{t \to \infty} \frac{C(t)}{t}$ is approximately equivalent to minimizing L when γ is small relative to μ.

Commenting on Dr. Weiss' remark, suppose that failure is detected with probability p, $0 < p \le 1$. Then if the system fails at time t where $x_i < t \le x_{i+1}$, the expected cost is easily calculated to be

$$c_1 \left(i + \frac{1}{p} \right) + c_2 \left[p \sum_{j=1}^{\infty} (1-p)^{j-1} x_{i+j} - t \right] .$$

For periodic checks at multiples of time x, $x_{i+j} = (i+j)x$ and the above expression becomes

$$c_1 \left(i + \frac{1}{p} \right) + c_2 \left[x \left(i + \frac{1}{p} \right) - t \right] = c_1 (i+1) + c_2 \left[x(i+1) - t \right] + \frac{1-p}{p} c_1 + \frac{1-p}{p} x c_2 .$$

Hence, for periodic procedures, the expected loss for imperfect checking $E_p[\text{Loss}]$, is related to the expected loss for perfect checking by

$$E_p[\text{Loss}] = E[\text{Loss}] + \frac{1-p}{p} c_1 + \frac{1-p}{p} x c_2 .$$

Thus in the periodic case a neat answer does exist. Note, further, that when $E[\text{Loss}]$ is convex that $E_p[\text{Loss}]$ is convex and

$$\frac{dE_p}{dx} = \frac{dE}{dx} + \frac{1-p}{p} c_2 .$$

Hence in this case the minimizing check interval for E_p is smaller than that of E.

Dr. Zelen's point is pertinent and one worth noting. To my knowledge, very little has been done on monitoring procedures in which one uses the information about system operation that is obtained by each check.

JOAN RAUP ROSENBLATT
Confidence limits for the reliability of complex systems

SUMMARY

This paper treats estimation of a probability R interpreted as "system reliability," when the estimate is to be based on data obtained from subsystem tests. A mathematical representation of the dependence of R on subsystem characteristics is assumed to be given. Procedures for obtaining lower confidence limits for R are studied. A general formulation of the problem is given leading to a widely applicable method for distribution-free estimation of R and calculation of approximate nonparametric confidence intervals. The application of the general method is illustrated in several particular cases. Comparisons with "exact" methods, and with alternative approximate methods are discussed.

1. Introduction

Predictions of system performance may be composed in various ways on the basis of system analysis and data which are available before the whole system has been tested. Frequently, the prediction is an estimate of the value of a probability, interpreted as "system reliability." Although other quantities are sometimes used to describe system performance, this paper is confined to the problem of estimating a probability associated with a system, using data obtained from tests of subsystems or components. In particular, methods are developed for calculating confidence limits.

The problem of confidence limits for system reliability is formulated in a general and fairly abstract form. A mathematical representation is assumed to be given relating relevant system characteristics to the quantities which can be measured in subsystem tests. System reliability is then expressed as a functional of the several distribution functions of subsystem characteristics (Section 2). This leads naturally to the development of approximate nonparametric confidence interval methods (Section 3). For the important special case where system reliability is expressed as a function of subsystem reliabilities, methods are indicated for obtaining approximate confidence limits for systems more complex than those for which exact methods are now available (Section 4). A survey of approximate methods proposed by other authors is included in Section 4. Additional parametric cases are discussed, and some preliminary results are given on comparisons between the exact and the nonparametric methods and on the robustness of the exact methods (Sections 5 and 6). Further problems and possible generalizations are discussed briefly (Section 7).

Acknowledgments. A prepublication draft of this paper was distributed to conference participants and to a number of other persons. Comments and suggestions from a number of people have been incorporated in the present version. I am indebted to John K. Abraham E. L. Crow, and W. A. Thompson, Jr., for their careful reading of the manuscript, which contributed to the elimination of errors and obscurities. A point raised by J. D. Esary during the discussion of the paper (and also by Abraham) has led to some amplification and clarification in Section 4. Remaining faults are, of course, mine.

A. Madansky and M. Lipow kindly sent copies of their unpublished reports, and the unpublished memoranda by F. Nishime were made available by L. A. Aroian. The numerical examples in Section 6 were prepared by Anna M. Glinski.

2.   General Formulation of the Problem

Consider a system whose performance can be described by the value of some quantity denoted by x_0 . This may be the numerical value of some output of the system. In one particular case of special importance, x_0 has the value "one" if system performance is satisfactory for a specified length of time, and x_0 has the value "zero" otherwise. In a second particular case, x_0 is the "lifetime" of the system. In general, suppose that the performance of the system is satisfactory if the value of x_0 is at least as large as a specified number c .

Now, suppose that there is an ensemble of "copies" of the system —actual or hypothetical—and suppose that the value of x_0 is not the same for all "copies." Consider the distribution of the values of x_0 in an ensemble of systems to be a probability distribution. The "reliability" of a system selected from the ensemble is then defined by

$$R = Pr(X_0 \geq c) .\tag{1}$$

The capital letter X_0 is used to denote a random variable whose probability distribution is given by the distribution of values of the quantity x_0 in the ensemble of systems.

If a number of "copies" of the system are available for testing, it is possible to estimate R after determining the value of x_0 for each system tested. The simplest and most generally valid procedure for estimating R would be to count the number of tested systems for which x_0 exceeds the prescribed value c . The estimate of R is then a random variable with binomial distribution. A confidence interval would be estimated by standard statistical techniques. If the distribution of X_0 is known, except for the values of a few parameters, then there may be other statistical procedures available for estimating R and confidence limits for R .[1]

Consider now the mathematical representation of the dependence of system reliability on the characteristics of subsystems. Suppose that the value of x_0 , which describes system performance, can be equated to a function of the values of certain characteristics $x_1, x_2, \ldots, x_k$ of subsystems. That is, suppose there is a given function

$$x_0 = f(x_1, x_2, \ldots, x_k) \quad . \tag{2}$$

The probability distribution of X_0 then depends through this relationship on the probability distributions of random variables $X_1, \ldots, X_k$ associated with subsystem characteristics. The ensemble of systems for which we are interested in the distribution of values of x_0 is identified with the ensemble of systems which could be constructed by assembling subsystems with characteristics $x_1, \ldots, x_k$. Each subsystem is drawn from an ensemble of like subsystems, so that the probability distribution of the random variable X_i is the distribution of the value of x_i in the ensemble of subsystems of the $i\underline{th}$ type.

Now the problem of estimating

$$R = Pr(X_0 \geq c)$$

has been converted into the problem of estimating

$$R = Pr[f(X_1, \ldots, X_k) \geq c] \quad . \tag{3}$$

It is assumed that the random variables $X_1, X_2, \ldots, X_k$ are statistically independent. In fact, without this assumption the estimation problem is essentially unsolvable; independently performed

---

[1] Confidence interval methods using data obtained from system tests are not discussed in this paper. No attempt will be made to give references to the general literature of statistics, but it may be noted that application of the general methodology in reliability problems has been discussed by Bazovsky (1961), Gryna et al (1960), Lloyd and Lipow (1962), Madansky (1958), and others.

subsystem tests can yield information concerning the marginal distribution of each subsystem characteristic, but not concerning the joint distribution of two or more. The apparent starkness of the independence assumption may be mitigated somewhat, however, since nothing in the present general formulation of the estimation problem precludes the possibility that one or more of the subsystem characteristics x_i might be a vector variable.

Let $F_1(.), F_2(.), \ldots, F_k(.)$ denote the cumulative distributions of the random variables $X_1, \ldots, X_k$, respectively. The expression (3) for R may now be written,

$$ R = \int \ldots \int \Phi(x_1, \ldots, x_k) \, dF_1(x_1) \, \ldots \, dF_k(x_k) \; , \qquad (4) $$

where $\Phi(x_1, \ldots, x_k)$ is the characteristic function of the set $\{(x_1, \ldots, x_k) : f(x_1, \ldots, x_k) \geq c\}$,

$$ \Phi = \begin{cases} 1 & \text{if } f \geq c \, , \\ 0 & \text{otherwise} \, . \end{cases} $$

More briefly, (4) may be written

$$ R = E \Phi(X_1, \ldots, X_k) \; , \qquad (4') $$

where E denotes expectation with respect to the distributions of $X_1, \ldots, X_k$. The representation (4) for R will be employed in the development of approximate confidence interval procedures.

In the form (4), R has been represented as a regular functional of the distribution functions $F_1, \ldots, F_k$, in the sense of Hoeffding (1948). The general theory of unbiased estimation of such functionals will be applied.

The validity of all procedures for estimating R through the function f depends (of course) on the accuracy of f as a representation of x_0 in terms of the subsystem quantities $x_1, \ldots, x_k$.

2.1. Confidence Limits for R. This paper treats the calculation of lower confidence limits for R, using the results of independently conducted subsystem tests.

It is assumed that a sample of n_i values of x_i has been obtained $(i = 1, \ldots, k)$. Let these subsystem data be denoted briefly by z (and the corresponding random variable by Z). In general, z is a vector of dimension $(n_1 + \ldots + n_k)$. The components of the vector random variable Z are assumed to be mutually independent. In cases where subsystem characteristics are assumed to have distributions of a specified form, the individual observations on each subsystem may be replaced by sufficient statistics for the parameters of these distributions and the dimension of z would be correspondingly reduced.[2]

A lower confidence limit procedure for R is given by a function L(z), depending also on the sample sizes and the confidence level (1-α), such that

$$\Pr \{L(Z) \leq R \} = (1 - \alpha) \ . \tag{5}$$

If any of the underlying distributions $F_1, \ldots, F_k$ are discrete, (t) is replaced by

$$\Pr \{L(Z) \leq R \} \geq (1 - \alpha) \ . \tag{5'}$$

It may be remarked here that L(z) is not necessarily a monotonic function of a point estimator $\hat{R}(z)$, although it may be if there is an estimator $\hat{R}(z)$ whose distribution depends only on R . This point has been discussed in some detail by Buehler (1956, 1957).

2.2. The "Simulation" Idea. Before the details of notation are introduced for the general method of unbiased estimation of R , some motivation will be given by showing its relation to procedures which have been suggested in various forms, in connection with the problem of confidence limits for reliability.

The simplest and most generally applicable procedure for estimating R through $f(x_1, \ldots, x_k)$ is as follows: Obtain test results for the subsystem characteristics $x_1, \ldots, x_k$. Using each test result only once, calculate a set of values of $f(x_1, \ldots, x_k)$. That is, numerically "build" a set of systems out of the tested subsystems, using each subsystem not more than once. The proportion of times that the calculated value of x_0 exceeds c , R_1 , is an estimate of R . Once again, binomial distribution theory applies. It is not necessary to know anything about the probability distributions of $X_1, \ldots, X_k$ in order to apply this procedure.

This is essentially the same as the suggestion which has been made by a number of authors, for the case of "zero-one" components.

---

[2] It is appropriate to note here another set of relevant topics not discussed in this paper, namely, results on approximate distributions of products or other functions of random variables having specified distributions. In certain cases, when the forms of the distributions $F_1, \ldots, F_k$ are specified, an estimate of R is obtainable as a function of estimates of the parameters of $F_1, \ldots, F_k$. For some very special cases, the distribution of $\hat{R}$ has a known form (see Sections 5 and 6). More commonly, the estimates of parameters of the individual F_i would have known distributions but the distribution of the estimate of R would have to be approximated.

See Connor and Wells (1962), De Cicco (1959), Garner and Vail (1961), Lloyd and Lipow (1962), the present author (1955b) and perhaps others. Some of these authors have suggested modifications of this simple technique, which will be noted as appropriate.

It is intuitively clear that the procedure just described provides validity at the expense of "inefficient" use of data. First, if the number of subsystem tests for one subsystem is small, then only a small number of system results can be constructed numerically, other data are discarded. Second, there is an element of arbitrariness since the confidence interval obtained by this procedure depends on the outcome of the randomization of assignments of subsystem results to "systems."

One "improved" procedure would be to "build" numerically all possible systems which could be assembled using the subsystems which were tested, i. e., using all possible combinations of k values $x_1, \ldots, x_k$. This provides a better (under suitable conditions, a minimum variance unbiased) point estimate of R, but it is not possible to go on to calculate confidence limits immediately, since the distribution of this estimate of R, the fraction $\hat{R}_2$ of successes in all possible systems, does not usually depend only on R.

The estimate $\hat{R}_1$ may be interpreted as the result of a single series of hypothetical system tests, computed for assemblies constructed numerically from subsystem test data. The estimate $\hat{R}_2$ would accordingly be interpreted as the average of the values of $\hat{R}_1$ which would be obtained if the procedure were repeated over and over using random assignment of subsystem data to the hypothetical systems. This interpretation suggests that $\hat{R}_2$ be called the "simulation" estimate of R.[3]

Lloyd and Lipow (1962) present a procedure (attributed by them to D. L. Lindstrom and J. H. Madden) which eliminates the arbitrary feature of the simple method. The simple method provides a binomially distributed estimate $\hat{R}_1$ of R, based on a sample of m "simulated system tests," where m is the smallest subsystem sample size. The Lindstrom-Madden procedure is to treat the "improved" point estimate $\hat{R}_2$ as if it were the fraction of successes in m trials with success probability R (see Section 3.2 for details). Lloyd and Lipow report that for samples of equal size and 2 or 3 "zero-one" subsystems, this method leads to confidence limits "almost identical" with exact limits obtained by the procedure developed by Buehler (1957). Results obtained by the present author (1955b) suggest that this method should

---

[3] Note that the "simulation" considered here is based on given subsystem test results. It is different from the sort of completely hypothetical simulation which is sometimes used in "statistical tolerancing." The latter is based on subsystem "data" generated as random numbers from specified distributions.

tend to be conservative, especially for large sample sizes, since the variance of $\hat{R}_2$ is always less than or equal to $\mathrm{Var}\,(\hat{R}_1) = R(1-R)/m$ (see Section 4 below.) •

Connor and Wells (1962) suggest that the conditional distribution of $\hat{R}_1$ be calculated, given the sample results for zero-one subsystems, and that the conditional expectation of a confidence limit calculated from $\hat{R}_1$ might be used as a confidence limit for R . They have not yet reported results on the accuracy of this approximation. The approximate method of Garner and Vail, discussed below in Section 4, is related to the Connor-Wells method.

The "simulation" idea has great intuitive appeal. For zero-one subsystems, it is in addition easy to calculate the estimate $\hat{R}_2$ and to employ the presumably conservative Lindstrom-Madden confidence interval procedure. For more general relations $x_0 = f(x_1, \ldots, x_k)$, the numerical evaluation of x_0 for all possible combinations of subsystem test results may be more difficult. But, in the general case, the "simulation" estimate $\hat{R}_2$ is a nonparametric minimum variance unbiased estimate of R which is known to have asymptotic normal distribution (under suitable conditions). An investigation of approximate confidence interval procedures based on the normal approximation, or improved approximations, promises to be fruitful. The remainder of this paper summarizes the main points of the underlying theory and reports the methods and results of early steps in the investigation.

3. The General Estimate of R and Its Distribution

The "simulation" estimate of R is a U-statistic (Hoeffding, 1948). The application of the theorems of Hoeffding's 1948 paper to two-sample statistics was indicated by Lehmann (1951). A specialization of the same theorems for certain two-sample statistics was presented by Hoeffding in lectures on nonparametric statistics in 1949-1950, and was developed further with particular reference to two-sample U-statistics for functionals with kernel $\Phi = 0$ or 1 by Rosenblatt (1955a). The k-sample results considered here are immediate generalizations of the foregoing.

Let $(x_{i1}, \ldots, x_{i\,n_i})$ denote the subsystem data for the $i^{\underline{th}}$ subsystem $(i = 1, \ldots, k)$. That is, x_{ij} is an observed value of the random variable X_i whose distribution is F_i .

The "simulation" estimate of R , denoted by $\hat{R}_2$ in the preceding section, will be denoted henceforward by U , and may be written

$$U = \Sigma' \Phi(x_{1i_1}, \ldots, x_{ki_k})/n_1, \ldots, n_k \,, \qquad\qquad 6$$

where Σ' denotes k-fold summation over $1 \leq i_j \leq n_j$, $j = 1, \ldots, k$.

The statistic U obviously provides an unbiased estimate of
$R = E\Phi$ (recall equations (4) and (4')).

It was remarked above that, under suitable conditions, U is a
minimum variance unbiased estimator for R . Sufficient conditions
may be found following Halmos (1946), for example. Roughly speaking, the set of allowable distributions $F_1, F_2, \ldots, F_k$ must be rather
large, including a large class of discrete distributions.

To describe the asymptotic distribution of U , some additional
notation is defined. Let

$$\Psi_i(x_i) = E\Phi(X_1, \ldots, X_{i-1}, x_i, X_{i+1}, \ldots, X_k) - R , \qquad (7)$$

where expectation is taken with respect to the (k-1) random variables.
Then let

$$\xi_i = E\Psi_i^2(X_i), \quad i = 1, \ldots, k . \qquad (8)$$

It can be shown that

$$\text{Var } U = \sum_{i=1}^{k} \xi_i/n_i + O(1/m^2) , \qquad (9)$$

where $m = \min(n_1, \ldots, n_k)$. The remainder term is always non-
negative, and

$$\text{Var } U \leq R(1-R)/m . \qquad (10)$$

If the sample sizes n_i tend to infinity in such a way that
$n_i \sim a_i m$ (i = 1, \ldots, k) where the a_i are fixed constants, then $V = \sqrt{m}(U-R)$ is asymptotically normally distributed as $m \to \infty$ with
variance

$$\sigma^2(V) = \sum_{i=1}^{k} \xi_i/a_i . \qquad (11)$$

The ξ_i are, of course, nuisance parameters. But they will be
seen to be regular functionals, which can in turn be estimated by k-
sample U-statistics $\hat{\xi}_i$. Let $\hat{\sigma}^2(V)$ denote the estimate of $\sigma^2(V)$
obtained when the $\hat{\xi}_i$ are substituted in (11). Approximate confidence limits for R are based on the proposition that $\sqrt{m}(U-R)/\hat{\sigma}(V)$
is asymptotically normally distributed as $m \to \infty$, provided $\sigma(V) > 0$.

Since the notation required for amplifying the results summarized
in the preceding paragraph is cumbersome, the estimation of $\sigma^2(V)$
will be discussed only for the case of k = 2 subsystems. The extension to $k \geq 3$ involves chiefly a proliferation of notation.

From (7) and (8), ξ_1 may be written

$$\xi_1 = E\,K_1(X_1, X'_1, X_2, X'_2) \ , \tag{12}$$

where X_i, X'_i are independent random variables distributed according to F_i , and

$$2K_1 = [\Phi(x_1, x_2) - \Phi(x'_1, x_2)] \cdot [\Phi(x_1, x'_2) - \Phi(x'_1, x'_2)] \ .$$

Now K_1 is a symmetric function of each pair of arguments (x_i, x'_i) and the U-statistic estimator for ξ_1 is given by

$$2n_1(n_1-1)n_2(n_2-1)\hat{\xi}_1 = \sum_{h \neq i}\sum_{j \neq k} K_1(x_{1h}, x_{1i}, x_{2j}, x_{2k}) \ . \tag{13}$$

For computation, this reduces to

$$n_1(n_1-1)n_2(n_2-1)\hat{\xi}_1 = n_1 T_1 + T_2 + n_1 n_2 U - n_1^2 n_2^2 U^2 \ , \tag{14}$$

where

$$T_1 = \sum_h \sum_{j \neq k} \Phi(x_{1h}, x_{2j})\,\Phi(x_{1h}, x_{2k}) \ , \tag{15}$$

$$T_2 = \sum_{h \neq i} \sum_j \Phi(x_{1h}, x_{2j})\,\Phi(x_{1i}, x_{2j}) \ . \tag{16}$$

In (13), (15), and (16), the indexes are summed over the ranges $1 \leq h$, $i \leq n_1$ and $1 \leq j$, $k \leq n_2$.

An equation corresponding to (12) may be written for ξ_2 ; but the estimation formula corresponding to (14) may be obtained from (14) by symmetry—interchange n_1, n_2 and T_1, T_2 .

3.1. Calculation Formulas, k = 2.

Now calculating the value of U , and use of formula (14) involve evaluation of $\Phi(x_1, x_2)$ for $n_1 n_2$ pairs of sample values of x_1, x_2 —and, for (14), further combinations of these values are required. Each evaluation of $\Phi(x_1, x_2)$ consists of evaluating $f(x_1, x_2)$ and comparing the result with c . In general, this would be a formidable task, In particular cases, however, it may be possible to develop more specific formulas. This possibility is illustrated by the following.

Suppose the inequality $f(x_1, x_2) \geq c$ can be rewritten in the form $h(x_1) \geq g(x_2, c)$. Suppose that all the numbers $h(x_{1i})$ and $g(x_{2j}, c)$ are distinct. Then define the ordered values of $h(x_{1i})$ and $g(x_{2j}, c)$:

$$h_{(1)} \leq h_{(2)} \leq \cdots \leq h_{(n_1)} \ ,$$

$$g_{(1)} \geq g_{(2)} \geq \cdots \geq g_{(n_2)} \ .$$

(Notice that the h's are numbered in increasing order of magnitude while the g's are numbered in decreasing order.) Combine the two sets of values and define

$$r_i = \text{rank of } h_{(i)}$$

$$s_j = \text{rank of } g_{(j)} \ .$$

Then it can be shown that

$$n_1 n_2 U = \sum_{i=1}^{n_1} (r_i - i) \ , \tag{17}$$

$$T_1 = 2 \sum_{j=1}^{n_2} (n_2 - j)(n_1 + n_2 + 1 - j - s_j) \ , \tag{18}$$

$$T_2 = 2 \sum_{i=1}^{n_1} (n_1 - i)(r_i - i) \ . \tag{19}$$

For example, if $f(x_1, x_2) = x_1 + x_2$, then $h(x_1) = x_1$ and $g(x_2, c) = c - x_2$; if $f(x_1, x_2) = x_1^2 + x_2^2$, then $h(x_1) = x_1^2$ and $g(x_2, c) = c - x_2^2$.

The derivation of these formulas shows that for $k \geq 3$ the calculation of $n_1 n_2 \ldots n_k$ values of f may be reduced to the calculation of $(n_1 n_2 \ldots n_r + n_{r+1} \ldots n_k)$ values of auxiliary functions h and g , whose ranks are used in formulas similar to (17) - (19). Other methods may be available for different types of special cases.

3.2 . Approximate Confidence Limits. The general estimator U for R , with information about its distribution, may be used with several approaches to obtaining approximate confidence limits.

First, it would be possible to treat U (by the Lindstrom-Madden procedure) as if it were binomially distributed with parameters R and $m = \min(n_1, \ldots, n_k)$. For large m , this procedure would be valid but conservative, since $R(1-R)/m$ tends to over-estimate the asymptotic variance of U . For moderate sample sizes, however, this might turn out to work well enough. Generally, of course, U will not have one of the values i/m ($i = 0, 1, \ldots, m$) . A convention is required which will determine how a lower confidence limit for R is to be determined from U and m . When m is very large, it would be reasonable to replace U by $[mU]/m$, where $[mU]$ denotes the integer part of mU . For small or moderately large values of m , it might be advantageous to interpolate between the lower confidence limits associated with $[mU]$ and $[mU+1]$. Either linear interpolation or graphical interpolation from charts for binomial confidence limits might be considered.

Second, it has been seen that the asymptotic variance $\sigma^2(V)$

can be estimated and that $\sqrt{m}$ (U–R) $/\hat{\sigma}(V) = 0$ is approximately normally distributed for large m.   It is not known yet how large m must be
in order that this approximation be satisfactory, particularly if R is
close to unity. Observe, in particular, that $\hat{\sigma}(U) = 0$ and the method
fails whenever U = 1. It may be that for moderately large sample sizes it
will be better to estimate the exact instead of the asymptotic variance
of U.   P. K. Sen (1960) has given conditions under which a consistent
estimate of the variance of a U–statistic may be obtained.

A particular two-sample nonparametric problem for which estimation
of and confidence limits for a probability have been studied is the case
$R = Pr(X_1 < X_2)$, which has been considered by Z. W. Birnbaum (1956).

The advantages of any approximate method based on U are that it
is not necessary to make assumptions about the form of the underlying
distributions $F_1, \ldots, F_k$, and that the point estimate U has the useful
"simulation" interpretation.

4. "Zero-One" Components

The general approach discussed above may be specialized for the
case where each of the subsystem characteristics is represented by
a zero-one variable, and system reliability is expressed as a function of subsystem reliabilities.

The discussion of this specialization will be brief, since this
case may be (and has been) treated by methods less elaborate than
those of this paper. See Abraham (1962), Buehler (1956, 1957), De
Cicco (1959), Lipow (1958, 1959, 1961), Lloyd and Lipow (1962),
Madansky (1960), Steck (1957), Thomas (1960), and perhaps
others. In particular, methods studied for this case include (i) exact
methods, with some tables for k = 2, 3, (ii) asymptotic approximations which will probably turn out to be more accurate than the normal
approximation developed for the general nonparametric problem, and
(iii) a variety of approximate methods whose comparative properties
remain to be determined. This section includes a brief review of the
literature on confidence interval methods for the case of zero-one
components.

A widely used simple type of mathematical model for system reliability represents the system as an assembly of subsystems or components, each of which either performs or fails.   In the simplest
case, all subsystems must perform in order that the system perform.
The mathematical representation of such a "series system" may be
written $x_0 = f(x_1, \ldots, x_k) = x_1 x_2 \cdots x_k$,

where each of the variables $x_0, x_1, \ldots, x_k$ equals one ("performs")
or zero ("fails"). More complicated systems have some redundant
subsystems and the "structure function" $f(x_1, \ldots, x_k)$ has a more
complicated form.   Birnbaum, Esary, and Saunders (1961) have
studied the properties of structure functions and the reliability of
a svstem represented by a structure function.   The structure function

is defined below in a particular standard form convenient for the purposes of this paper.

Consider the set of 2^k vectors $(x_1, \ldots, x_k)$, each denoting a combination of satisfactory and failed subsystems. Some of these correspond to satisfactory system performance; the others correspond to system failure. For each vector associated with satisfactory performance, write a product of k factors containing x_i if $x_i = 1$ and $(1-x_i)$ if $x_i = 0$. The structure function $f(x_1, \ldots, x_k)$ is defined to be the sum of these products, including one term for each vector corresponding to satisfactory system performance. The resulting function could usually be simplified by combining terms and using the fact that the variable x_i are idempotent. But equations (20) and (21) are valid in general only if f is a linear function of each of the x_i; it is convenient to assume that f is defined in the standard form stated above.

For k statistically independent components or subsystems, $R = \Pr(X_0 = 1)$, i.e., $c = 1$, and

$$R = f(p_1, \ldots, p_k) , \tag{20}$$

where $p_i = \Pr(X_i = 1)$, $i = 1, \ldots, k$. Furthermore, if p_i is estimated by the proportion of successes $\hat{p}_i$ in n_i tests of the $i\underline{\text{th}}$ subsystem, then

$$U = f(\hat{p}_1, \ldots, \hat{p}_k) . \tag{21}$$

Modifications may be made for the case when a component type is used more than once while its reliability is estimated from one sample. This case will not be considered here. See Buehler (1956).

The formula (11) for the asymptotic variance of U in terms of $\xi_1, \ldots, \xi_k$ is equivalent to the approximate formula for the variance of U which is obtained from the linear terms of a Taylor expansion of $f(x_1, \ldots, x_k)$ about $(p_1, \ldots, p_k)$. Asymptotic normality of U follows simply from theorems on the asymptotic normality of functions of sample moments (See, e.g., Cramér, 1946).

The development of exact confidence limits for R for this case, where the lower confidence limit $L(Z)$ is a function of $\hat{p}_1, \ldots, \hat{p}_k$, has been treated by Buehler and Steck. Extensive tables were prepared for series systems with $k = 2, 3$ by Lipow; these tables alone occupy several inches of bookshelf space, so that the desirability of approximate methods is evident.

De Cicco, Lloyd and Lipow, and Rosenblatt (1955b) consider the normal approximation. Madansky (1960) has suggested a chi-square approximation based on the proposition that $-2 \log \lambda$ is distributed approximately as chi-square when λ is a likelihood ratio statistic. Both of these approximations are inapplicable when there are no observed failures.

The variance of U attains its maximum $R(1-R)/m$ only if

$p_i = 1$ for all but one subsystem, the $j\underline{th}$ subsystem (say), and $p_j = R$ and $n_j = m$. Thus the Lindstrom-Madden procedure discussed earlier should tend to be conservative except for this "least favorable" type of situation.

When the normal approximation is to be used, general methods of the preceding section may be applied to obtain formulas for the ξ_i and for the estimates $\hat{\xi}_i$. For example, when $R = p_1 p_2$,

$$\xi_1 = p_1 (1 - p_1) p_2^2 \tag{22}$$

and

$$\hat{\xi}_1 = n_1 \hat{p}_1 (1 - \hat{p}_1) \hat{p}_2 (n_2 \hat{p}_2 - 1) / (n_1 - 1)(n_2 - 1) . \tag{23}$$

It may or may not be advantageous to use this unbiased estimate (23) of ξ_1 instead of substituting $\hat{p}_1$ and $\hat{p}_2$ in (22).

Madansky considers the likelihood ratio statistic appropriate for testing the (composite) null hypothesis

$$H_0 : f(p_1, \ldots, p_k) = R ,$$

where f is the structure function. Suppose s_i successes are observed in n_i tests of the $i\underline{th}$ subsystem. Let $b(s, n, p)$ denote the probability of s successes in n trials with success probability p . Then the likelihood ratio statistic is

$$Q(R) = \frac{\displaystyle\max_{f=R} \prod_{i=1}^{k} b(s_i, n_i, p_i)}{\displaystyle\max_{0 \le p_i \le 1} \prod_{i=1}^{k} b(s_i, n_i, p_i)} ,$$

and the $(1-\alpha)$-level confidence interval for R contains values of R for which

$$-2 \ln Q(R) \le \chi^2 (1-\alpha) ,$$

where $\chi^2 (1-\alpha)$ is the upper 100α percentage point of the chi-square distribution with one degree of freedom. Madansky has obtained explicit formulas for the confidence limits for a series system and for a parallel system.

Additional approximate formulas have been suggested for series systems, which should be included in any comparative study of confidence limit procedures. These formulas are stated briefly here.

Abraham (1962) derives bounds for $R = p_1 \ldots p_k$ under the condition

$\xi = \Sigma n_i(1-p_i)$; e.g., if $n_1 = \ldots = n_k = m$, then

$$1 - \xi/m \leq R \leq (1-\xi/mk)^k .$$

He then proposes a binomial or Poisson approximation for the distribution of

$$Y = \sum_{i=1}^{k} n_i(1 - \hat{p}_i)$$

and accordingly for confidence limits for $\xi = EY$. If ξ^* is an upper limit for ξ , then $1-\xi^*/m$ is a lower limit for R in the equal-sample-size case.

Garner and Vail (1961) and Connor and Wells (1962) suggest two variants of a procedure related to the "simple" statistic $\hat{R}_1$ discussed in Section 2. If $m = \min(n_1, \ldots, n_k)$ is the smallest sample size, then $m\hat{R}_1$ is the number of satisfactory systems obtained by random assembly of subsystem data into m systems. Suppose f_i failures are observed in the n_i tests of the $i\underline{th}$ subsystem, and let

$$r_0 = \max (f_1, \ldots, f_k) ,$$

$$r_1 = f_1 + \ldots + f_k .$$

Assume $r_1 < m$ (as it will be in any practical case). Now the value of $m\hat{R}_1$ will lie between the limits

$$m - r_1 \leq m\hat{R}_1 \leq m - r_0 .$$

Let $L(r)$ denote the lower confidence limit for binomial p when r successes are observed in m trials, and calculate $L(r)$ for $m - r_1 \leq r \leq m - r_0$. Both of the suggested procedures are weighted averages of the numbers $L(r)$.

Garner and Vail suggest that the $L(r)$ be weighted in proportion to the probability of observing r successes in m trials when the probability of success is $U = \hat{p}_1\hat{p}_2 \ldots \hat{p}_k$. Let

$$b(r) = \binom{m}{r} U^r(1-U)^{m-r} .$$

Then the Garner-Vail lower limit for R is given by

$$\sum_{r=m-r_1}^{m-r_0} L(r) b(r) \Big/ \sum_{r=m-r_1}^{m-r_0} b(r) .$$

Connor and Wells suggest that the conditional distribution of $\hat{R}_1$ be calculated for random assemblies with fixed $n_1, \ldots, n_k$ and

$f_1, \ldots, f_k$. Let $W(r)$ denote the conditional probability that $m\hat{R}_1 = r$. Then the Connor-Wells formula is

$$\sum_{r=m-r_1}^{m-r_0} L(r) W(r) \quad ,$$

the mean of the conditional distribution of $L(\hat{R}_1)$.

Nishime (1960) suggests a different formula involving confidence limits for binomial p . According to Aroian (1962), this formula works well for small sample sizes. Let s_i denote the number of successes observed in n_i trials of the $i\underline{th}$ subsystem, and let $L(s, n)$ denote the lower limit for binomial p when s successes are observed in n trials. Define

$$G = L(s_1 + \ldots + s_k , n_1 + \ldots + n_k) \quad ,$$

$$G_i = L(s_i, n_i) \quad .$$

Then the Nishime formula for a lower confidence limit for R is

$$L = \left(\frac{kG}{G_1 + \ldots + G_k} \right)^k G_1 \ldots G_k \quad .$$

5. Exponential Lifetime Distributions

The problem of confidence intervals for mean lifetime has been extensively studied, beginning with the work of Epstein and Sobel (1953) on life-testing methods for the exponential distribution. A recent paper by Goodman and Madansky (1962) deals with confidence intervals for the reliability of components with exponentially distributed lifetimes, and especially with one-sided tolerance limits for the exponential distribution (i.e., one-sided confidence limits for specified percentiles). Apparently very little work has been done on confidence intervals for the reliability of systems composed of subsystems having exponentially distributed lifetimes. Since the exponential distribution model is frequently employed in making estimates of system reliability, some methods for studying confidence interval procedures in this case will be indicated. This discussion is restricted to the case of series systems, for which the rule "system failure rate equals sum of component failure rates" applies.

Consider a series system of k components each having exponential lifetime distribution,

$$1 - F_i(x) = \exp \{-x/\theta_i\} \quad , \quad x > 0 \quad , \quad i = 1, \ldots, k \quad . \quad (24)$$

The reliability of this system is defined to be the probability that it survives at least to time t . In the general notation of this paper,

$$x_0 = f(x_1, \ldots, x_k) = \min(x_1, \ldots, x_k) \qquad (25)$$

$$R = \Pr(X_0 \geq t) \qquad (26)$$

(i.e., c = t). Let $\theta*$ denote the harmonic mean of the component mean lifetimes,

$$\theta* = k\left(\frac{1}{\theta_1} + \ldots + \frac{1}{\theta_k}\right)^{-1} . \qquad (27)$$

Then (26) may be written

$$R = \exp\{-tk/\theta*\} . \qquad (28)$$

Since R is an increasing function of $\theta*$, a lower confidence limit for R may be obtained from a lower confidence limit for $\theta*$.

Let a sample of n_i observations from each of the k lifetime distributions be given, and let $\bar{x}_i$ (i = 1, ..., k) denote the corresponding sample means. An approximate confidence interval procedure for $\theta*$ (and hence for R) will be given, to be compared later with the approximate procedure that would be obtained from the general non-parametric method of this paper.

5.1. Approximate Confidence Limits for $\theta*$. The procedure to be given is exact when $n_1 = \ldots = n_k$ and $\theta_1 = \ldots = \theta_k$, and approximate when these conditions are not satisfied.

It is well known that $2n_i\bar{x}_i/\theta_i$ is distributed as $\chi^2_{2n_i}$ (chi-square with $2n_i$ degrees of freedom). Accordingly, by the additive property of chi-square, $2kn\bar{x}/\theta*$ is distributed approximately as χ^2_{2kn} , where $k\bar{x} = \bar{x}_1 + \ldots + \bar{x}_k$ and n is the harmonic mean of the n_i . Let $\chi^2_\gamma(1 - \alpha)$ be defined by

$$\Pr\{\chi^2_\gamma \leq \chi^2_\gamma(1 - \alpha)\} = 1 - \alpha .$$

Then, approximately, it is asserted at confidence level $(1-\alpha)$ that

$$\theta* \geq 2kn\bar{x}/\chi^2_{2kn}(1 - \alpha) . \qquad (29)$$

5.2. Comparison with the General Method. For a series system, with components having any lifetime distributions, the general method for this case reduces to that for the zero-one case treated in Section 4. Thus, for example, the quantities ξ_i which appear in the asymptotic variance of U are given by

$$\xi_i = R^2(1-p_i)/p_i , \quad i = 1, \ldots, k ,$$

with

$$p_i = \exp\{-t/\theta_i\} ,$$

when the lifetime distributions are exponential.

6. Additional illustrative Special Cases

In certain special cases, an exact lower confidence limit for R may be given, for simple functions $f(x_1, x_2)$ of two variables, under various assumptions concerning the probability distributions of X_1 and X_2 (Rosenblatt and Glinski, 1961). The examples selected were chosen because the calculation of confidence limits is possible, through use of known statistical techniques. The general approach followed in each example is to obtain the probability distribution of $X_0 = f(X_1, X_2)$, where this turns out to be a known distribution whose parameters depend on the parameters of the known distributions of X_1 and X_2. Then the system reliability is determined by the value of some function λ of the parameters of the distributions of X_1 and X_2. In fact, R turns out to be a monotonic (increasing or decreasing) function of λ, and a lower confidence limit for R is provided by a confidence limit (lower and upper respectively) for λ.

Each example is summarized as follows (derivations being omitted):

(1) Form of the function $f(x_1, x_2)$.
(2) Assumptions concerning the probability distributions of X_1 and X_2.
(3) Expression for $R = R(\lambda)$.
(4) Formula for estimating λ (and hence $R(\lambda)$).
(5) Formulas for (a) appropriate confidence limit M for λ and (b) lower confidence limit L for R.

The following standardized notation is used in all examples. The confidence coefficient is $(1-\alpha)$. $G(x|.)$ denotes a cumulative distribution function. The parameters and form of the distribution are given to the right of the vertical bar; thus, the cumulative distribution function

$$\frac{1}{\sigma\sqrt{2\pi}} \int_{-\infty}^{x} \exp[-(t-\mu)^2/2\sigma^2] dt$$

is written

$$G(x \mid \text{normal}, \mu, \sigma) .$$

The notation $K(u|.)$ denotes a percentage point, as defined by

$$G[K(u|.) \mid .] = u ,$$

where the specifications inserted after the vertical bars are identical. Thus, the percentage point corresponding to the upper 10% tail-probability of the F-distribution with ν_1 and ν_2 degrees of freedom is written

$$K(.90 \mid \text{F-dist.}, \nu_1, \nu_2) \ .$$

Sample means are denoted $\bar{x}_1$ and $\bar{x}_2$, n_1 and n_2 are the sample sizes, and other functions of the sample values are defined as needed.

EXAMPLE 1.

(1) $f(x_1, x_2) = x_1 + x_2$

(2) X_1 and X_2 are normally distributed with unknown means μ_1, μ_2 and known standard deviations σ_1 and σ_2.

(3) $\begin{cases} R = G[(\mu_1 + \mu_2 - c)/\sqrt{\sigma_1^2 + \sigma_2^2} \mid \text{normal, } 0, 1] \\ \lambda = \mu_1 + \mu_2 \end{cases}$

(4) $\hat{\lambda} = \bar{x}_1 + \bar{x}_2$

(5a) $M = \bar{x}_1 + \bar{x}_2 - K(1-\alpha \mid \text{normal, } 0, 1) \sqrt{\dfrac{\sigma_1^2}{n_1} + \dfrac{\sigma_2^2}{n_2}}$

(5b) $L = G[(M-c)/\sqrt{\sigma_1^2 + \sigma_2^2} \mid \text{normal, } 0, 1]$

EXAMPLE 2

(1) $f(x_1, x_2) = x_1 + x_2$

(2) X_1 and X_2 are normally distributed with unknown means μ_1, μ_2 and unknown variances σ_1^2, σ_2^2 with $\rho^2 = \sigma_1^2/\sigma_2^2$ known.

(3) $\begin{cases} R = (\text{Same as in Example 1}) \\ \lambda = (\mu_1 + \mu_2 - c)/\sigma_2\sqrt{1 + \rho^2} \end{cases}$

(4) $\hat{\lambda} = (\bar{x}_1 + \bar{x}_2 - c)/s\sqrt{1 + \rho^2} \mid$

where

$$\rho^2(n_1 + n_2 - 2)s^2 = \sum_{j=1}^{n_1} (x_{1j} - \bar{x}_1)^2 + \rho^2 \sum_{j=1}^{n_2} (x_{2j} - \bar{x}_2)^2$$

(5a) A lower confidence limit for λ is given implicitly by the following equation which has to be solved for M :

$$\hat{\lambda}\sqrt{\frac{n_1 n_2 (1+\rho^2)}{n_1 + \rho^2 n_2}} = K\left(1-\alpha \mid \text{non-central-t, } n_1 + n_2 - 2, \ M\sqrt{\frac{n_1 n_2 (1+\rho^2)}{n_1 + \rho^2 n_2}}\right)$$

(5b) $L = G(M \mid \text{normal, } 0, 1)$

EXAMPLE 3

(1) $f(x_1, x_2) = x_1/x_2$.

(2) X_1/σ_1^2 and X_2/σ_2^2 are distributed as chi-square with ν_1 and ν_2 degrees of freedom, respectively, where ν_1 and ν_2 are known; σ_1^2 and σ_2^2 are unknown parameters.

(3) $\begin{cases} R = 1 - G\left(c \ \dfrac{\nu_2 \sigma_2^2}{\nu_1 \sigma_1^2} \ \middle| \ F\text{ - dist.}, \ \nu_1, \ \nu_2\right) \\ \lambda = \sigma_2^2 / \sigma_1^2 \end{cases}$

(4) $\hat{\lambda} = \nu_1 \bar{x}_2 / \nu_2 \bar{x}_1$

(5a) $M = \hat{\lambda} K(1-\alpha | F\text{- dist.}, \ n_1 \nu_1, \ n_2 \nu_2)$

(5b) $L = 1 - G(c \nu_2 M/\nu_1 \mid F \text{ - dist.}, \ \nu_1, \nu_2)$

Details of these examples, remarks on generalizations and special cases of them, three additional examples, and numerical illustrations are included in Rosenblatt and Glinski (1961).

A preliminary notion of the comparison between the exact method and the approximate U-statistic method under the conditions of Example 1 may be obtained from the following results, which were obtained by Miss Glinski. Five pairs of samples of ten normal deviates each were used. The constant c was chosen so that $R = .92$. Lower confidence limits were calculated at level $(1-\alpha) = 0.95$. The Lindstrom-Madden confidence limit was read from a chart which permitted (e.g.) $U = .98$ to be treated as the proportion of successes in 10 trials.

The exact results are, as would be expected, more "stable" for such small sample sizes. The normal approximation for the distribution of U , with estimated variance, is surprisingly satisfactory. The theoretical standard deviation of U in these numerical examples is 0.06, so that the distribution of U is clearly far from symmetrical. The Lindstrom-Madden approximation, on the other hand, appears to be excessively conservative.

| Sample | Point Estimates | | Confidence Limits | | |
| | | | Exact | Approximate | |
	U	$\hat{R}$	L	$U-(1.645)\hat{\sigma}(V)/\sqrt{m}$	Lindstrom-Madden
1	.98	.92	.82	.95	.72
2	.85	.86	.71	.71	.54
3	.77	.87	.72	.59	.46
4	.94	.92	.80	.87	.66
5	.95	.88	.74	.89	.68

7. Further Problems

The generalization to cover a reliability specification for a vector-valued x_0 would be of interest. In abstract terms, this case is covered by the methods given in the present paper, since a variable y_0 may be defined which equals one if and only if each component of the vector x_0 has a value within specification limits. The details for specific calculations would be somewhat more complicated. Generalizations for two-sided specifications $c_1 \le x_0 \le c_2$ would also be of interest, but would be relatively immediate.

Further investigations to establish conditions for the valid use of various approximations are, of course, required.

REFERENCES

Abraham, John K. (1962a), "A confidence interval for the reliability of multi-component systems," Proc. Seventh Conference on the Design of Experiments in Army Research Development and Testing (Fort Monmouth, 18-20 Oct. 1961), U.S. Army Research Office (Durham), ARODR 62-2, August 1962, pp. 483-518.

Abraham, John K. (1962b), Confidence intervals for the reliability of multi-component systems, Memorandum Report No. 1404, Ballistic Research Laboratories, Aberdeen Proving Ground, Md., May 1962.

Aroian, Leo A. (1962), "Some theoretical problems in reliability," Unpublished paper, presented before the Institute of Mathematical Statistics, Minneapolis, September 8, 1962.

Bazovsky, Igor (1961), Reliability Theory and Practice, Prentice Hall.

Birnbaum, Z.W. (1956), "On a use of the Mann-Whitney statistic," Proc. Third Berkeley Symposium, Univ. of Calif. Press, pp. 13-18.

Birnbaum, Z.W., J.D. Esary, and S.C. Saunders (1961), "Multi-component systems and structures and their reliability," Technometrics, Vol. 3, pp. 55-77.

Buehler, R.J. (1956), Theoretical considerations in determining confidence intervals for reliability, Unpublished manuscript.

Buehler, R.J. (1957), "Confidence limits for the product of two binomial parameters," Jour. Am. Stat. Assoc., Vol. 52, pp. 482-493.

Connor, W.S., and W.T. Wells (1962), "Simulating tests of a system from tests of its components," Proc. Eighth National Symposium on Reliability and Quality Control, pp. 14-16.

Cramér, H. (1946), Mathematical Methods of Statistics, Princeton Univ. Press.

De Cicco, Henry (1959), The reliability of weapon systems estimated from component data alone, Technical Note No. 1, Office for Reliability, Research and Effects (Reliability Branch - ORDSW-DR).

Epstein, B., and M. Sobel (1953), "Life Testing," J. Amer. Stat. Assoc., Vol. 48, pp. 486-502.

Garner, Norman R., and Richard W. Vail, Jr. (1961), "Confidence limits for systems reliability," Military Systems Design, Vol. 7, No. 5, Sept. -Oct.

Goodman, Leo, and Albert Madansky (1962), "Parameter-free and non-parametric tolerance limits: the exponential case," Techno-metrics, Vol. 4, No. 1, February, pp. 75-95.

Gryna, Frank M., Jr., et al., editors (1960), Reliability Training Text, American Society for Quality Control and Institute of Radio Engineers.

Halmos, P. R. (1946), "The theory of unbiased estimation," Ann. Math. Stat., Vol. 17, pp. 34-43.

Hoeffding, W. (1948), "A class of statistics with asymptotically normal distribution," Ann. Math. Stat., Vol. 19, pp. 293-325.

Lehmann, E. L. (1951), "Consistency and unbiasedness of certain nonparametric tests," Ann. Math. Stat., Vol. 22, pp. 165-179.

Lipow, M. (1958), Measurement of over-all reliability utilizing results of independent subsystem tests, GM-TR-0165-00506, Space Technology Laboratories (Reissued July 1959).

Lipow, M. (1959), Tables of upper confidence limits on failure probability of 1, 2 and 3 component serial systems, TR-50-0000-00756, Space Technology Laboratories (Reissued April 1960), 2 volumes.

Lipow, M. (1961), Tables of binomial upper confidence limits on probability of failure, 6120-0008-MU-000, Space Technology Laboratories.

Lloyd, D. K., and M. Lipow (1962), Reliability: Management, Methods, and Mathematics, Prentice-Hall.

Madansky, Albert (1958), "Uses of tolerance limits in missile evaluation," Proc. Statistical Techniques in Missile Evaluation Symposium Virginia Polytechnic Institute, August 5-8, pp. 43-52.

Madansky, Albert (1960), Approximate confidence limits for the reliability of series and parallel systems, RM-2552, The Rand Corporation, April 4.

Nishime, F. (1959), Techniques for... the establishment of confidence limits for the estimated reliability, Unpublished memorandum, Space Technology Laboratories, July 8, 1959.

Nishime, F. (1960), Derivation of Statistical criteria for flight failure penalties, Unpublished memorandum, Space Technology Laboratories, June 14, 1960.

Rosenblatt, J. R. (1955a), On a class of non-parametric tests, Institute of Statistics Mimeograph Series No. 138, University of North Carolina.

Rosenblatt, J. R. (1955b), On the probability of non-failure of an assembly of several components, Unpublished manuscript, National Bureau of Standards.

Rosenblatt, J. R., and Anna M. Glinski (1961), Confidence limits for reliability; Some illustrative examples in cases for which exact small sample methods are available, Unpublished working paper, National Bureau of Standards.

Sen, P. K. (1960), "On some convergence properties of U-statistics," Calcutta Statistical Assoc. Bulletin, Vol. 10, Nos. 37 and 38, pp. 1-18.

Steck, G. P. (1957), Upper confidence limits for the failure probability of complex networks, SC-4133(TR), Sandia Corporation. [Available from Office of Technical Services, Dept. of Commerce, Washington 25, D. C.]

Thomas, Ralph E. (1960), An improved formula for the standard deviation of the reliability product rule, Technical Report No. 2, Battelle Memorial Institute.

DISCUSSION OF THE PAPER BY DR. ROSENBLATT

George P. Steck.   The problem of constructing confidence intervals (in the Neyman sense) for the reliability of complex systems is one which the uninitiated often expect to dispose of quickly when they tackle it. However, even with all the effort so far expended on it, the problem remains—difficult and challenging.

Especially there remains the problem of small samples. This area is important not only for its own sake in obtaining the maximum reduction in the amount of testing required to prove out complex systems; but also, even though asymptotic methods are more convenient they will be useful only if they give useful answers, and this can be determined by extensive comparisons between asymptotic and exact results. (It is granted, however, that an asymptotic result could be a very poor approximation <u>mathematically</u> and yet be of great <u>practical</u> use.)

It is encouraging to have Mrs. Rosenblatt point out that what is an intuitively appealing procedure (i.e., simulation) also has some nice properties to recommend it. This is the first "optimum" result to appear in the literature of this subject. I hope it is not the last.

Mrs. Rosenblatt has also provided an excellent set of references in her paper, and I would like to amplify her discussion by brief mention of what some of the authors listed there have done with the problem.

Buehler (1956), as far as I know, has provided the most exhausting study of the small sample problem. His approach is to proceed directly from the definition of confidence limit. To fix the ideas, consider an upper α confidence limit for a system failure probability (αUCL for short), and let the vector of observations be $X = (X_1, X_2, \ldots, X_n)$ where X_i denotes the number of failures of the i<u>th</u> component. Loosely stated, the definition required is: given the vector of observations X , an αUCL for the failure probability q is the largest value of q consistent with the statement, "the probability of observing X or better is less than or equal to $1 - \alpha$."

The crux of the problem in this approach lies in the words "X or better." This phrase refers to an ordering on the sample space, and any ordering will yield a corresponding system of confidence intervals. If X is one dimensional then the best ordering is by magnitude and "X or better" becomes "X or fewer." If the dimension of X exceeds one there does not appear to be an ordering that is best in any overall sense.

Using an intuitive and computationally convenient ordering and the Poisson approximation to the binomial, Buehler generates some upper confidence limits for the product of two binomial parameters.

139

In addition, Steck (1957) and Lipow (1958) have applied Buehler's method to some other simple circuits.

De Cicco (1959) uses estimates of the mean and variance of system reliability (obtained by substituting estimates for population parameters into equations obtained from limited Taylor expansions of the reliability equation) together with Tschebycheff's inequality to construct his confidence intervals. Madansky (1960) constructs his intervals for series and/or parallel systems using the fact that $-2 \log$ (L is the likelihood ratio) has approximately a chi-square distribution with one degree of freedom.

Finally, I would like to mention some alternative approaches to the problem at hand which might conceivably prove fruitful. Often when a person is presented a problem he can't solve, he modifies the problem until he can solve it. So when presented an "impossible" circuit, I suggest replacing it by simpler circuits which approximate the original one. (The following discussion on approximate circuits was presented for me by Dr. James D. Esary of Boeing Scientific Research Laboratory, Seattle, Washington and is given here to the best of my needs and recollection.) Esary and Proschan[*] (1962) define the notions of "minimal path set" and "minimal cut set." Roughly speaking, a minimal path set is a set of components all of which must function before the system functions, and a minimal cut set is a set of components all of which must fail before the system fails. Now, if one constructs a circuit with the minimal paths in parallel and the elements of a minimal path in series and assumes the different minimal path sets to be independent, then the reliability of this circuit is no smaller than the reliability of the original circuit. Similarly, if one puts the minimal cuts in series, with the elements of a minimal cut in parallel, and assumes different minimal cut sets to be independent, one obtains an approximating circuit whose reliability does not exceed the reliability of the given circuit.

The result of all this is that one has two simpler approximate circuits whose reliabilities are upper and lower bounds to that of the given circuit. And if and when convenient methods are found for solving the series parallel and parallel series circuits, then one might expect the confidence limits so obtained would bound the ones desired for the original circuit.

Another idea which occurs to me is the following. Let the success or failure of the $i\underline{th}$ component be denoted by $X_i = 1$ or $X_i = 0$, respectively. If k items are in series then the proper operation of the series circuit is equivalent to $\min_{1 \le i \le k} X_i = 1$, and the proper

---

[*] J. D. Esary and F. Proschan, "Coherent Structures of Non-identical Components." Boeing Scientific Research Laboratory Report D1-82-015 February, 1962.

operation of a parallel circuit of these components is $\max\limits_{1 \le i \le k} X_i = 1$.

Since extreme values occur in this formulation, it is possible that the limiting distributions associated with extreme value theory might offer better approximations than the normal or chi-square distributions already in use.

J. D. Esary. Perhaps it is worth emphasizing that the validity of equation (20) depends upon the selection of a suitable form in writing the function $f(X_1, X_2, \ldots, X_k)$. For example, for the system consisting of component 1 in series with a parallel configuration of components 2 and 3

$$f(X_1, X_2, X_3) = 1 - (1 - X_1 X_2)(1 - X_1 X_3)$$

$$= X_1 X_2 + X_1 X_3 - X_1 X_2 X_3 \ .$$

Equation (20) holds for the second form for f but not the first.

Marvin Zelen. I believe there are many situations where the sample is the entire population. Rather than test components in a system, it is usually more practical to test the components themselves. Later on, these are to be assembled into a system. In this case, enumerating all ways of arranging components in a system constitutes the entire population.

Discussing this with Iz Rotkin, he pointed out another feature. Not only can one obtain the probability distribution of the system, but one could record which were the better components and use this information in assigning components to systems. It would be appreciated if he could elaborate on this a bit more.

I. Rotkin. I would like to carry out the assignment given to me by Marvin Zelen.

When all the components used to make complex assemblies are tested, there is an opportunity to generate "synthetic" statistics. All possible combinations of components can be tried by the methods outlined by Dr. Rosenblatt. In this way, artificial assemblies can be made. The number of such assemblies is of course much larger than the number of units that can actually be constructed or assembled from any given number of components. If the identities of the components and assemblies are maintained, it is then possible to select for actual construction only those combinations which have the desired characteristics. In this way, one can, within limits, control the statistical distribution of the characteristics of the assemblies manufactured from the pretested components.

Fred Frishmen. Let us consider a system consisting of two different and statistically independent components such that the system functions provided both components function. After testing "n" of these systems, an estimate of the population proportion effective $\hat{P}$ can be obtained. Further, a confidence interval (P_U, P_L) can be determined. In addition, by considering the two components, one can estimate the population proportion effective for each component and obtain the associated confidence intervals based on the "n" observations on each component. If a joint confidence interval, based on the two components, is constructed, how does this relate to the confidence interval based on the system proportion effective?

N. Mantel. In the life-table analog of the problem Frishman has raised, it is true that the limits on the overall survival rate are not affected by knowledge of the particular time interval in which failure occurred. This is the case, in particular, where no loss to follow up has occurred. A similar result should obtain in Frishman's case unless one assumes the 2 components operate independently and has knowledge of success or failure for each component or each trial, whatever may have been the outcome for the other component.

H. Reinhardt and M. Zelen. (The following was submitted after the seminar by H. Reinhardt and Zelen. It is an elaboration of one of the discussions.)
     Among the problems discussed by Dr. Rosenblatt is that of estimating the reliability of a series system where each component has an exponential failure law. It does not seem obvious how one would obtain the point estimate of the reliability of the system. We wish to elaborate on this problem in a different spirit from that of Dr. Rosenblatt's paper.
     Assume the system contains k independent components such that the $i^{\underline{th}}$ component has the probability density function (p. d. f.), $f_i(t, \lambda_i)$ where λ_i is the parameter associated with the p. d. f. and may be a vector quantity. Using Dr. Rosenblatt's notation, let $X_0 = f(X_1, X, \ldots, X_k)$ be the random variable which describes the system performance. Then the reliability of the system is defined to be

$$R(t \mid \lambda) \; = \; P_r\{X_0 > t \mid \lambda\} \; = \; \int_t^\infty g(x_0 \mid \lambda) \, dx_0 \tag{1}$$

where $g(x_0 \mid \lambda)$ is the p. d. f. of X_0 and $\lambda = (\lambda_1, \lambda_2, \ldots, \lambda_k)$.
(We have purposely written the l. h. s of (1) as a function of λ in order to emphasize that the reliability depends not only on t , but on λ also.)
     Let us further assume that there is prior information on

$\lambda_1, \lambda_2, \ldots, \lambda_k$ which can be expressed as a p. d. f. on $\lambda_1, \lambda_2, \ldots, \lambda_k$.
For this purpose, let $D'_i(\lambda_i)$ be the p. d. f. of this distribution for
λ_i (i = 1, 2, ..., k) . Then the prior expected value of $R(t|\lambda)$ is

$$R'(t) = \int_{-\infty}^{\infty} \int_{-\infty}^{\infty} \cdots \int_{-\infty}^{\infty} R(t|\lambda) D'_1(\lambda_1) D'_2(\lambda_2) \ldots D'_k(\lambda_k) d\lambda_1 d\lambda_2 \ldots d\lambda_k .$$
(2)

On the other hand, if a sample of n_i components of type i are
placed on life test, resulting in the observed time-to-failure
$x_i = (x_{i1}, x_{i2}, \ldots, x_{in_i})$, then we will have a posterior distribution
on λ . The posterior distribution is given by

$$D_i(\lambda_i|x_i) = \frac{D'_i(\lambda_i) \ell_i(x_i|\lambda_i)}{\int_{-\infty}^{\infty} D'_i(\lambda_i) \ell_i(x_i|\lambda_i) d\lambda_i}$$
(3)

where $\ell_i(x_i|\lambda_i) = \prod_{j=1}^{n_i} f(x_{ij}, \lambda_i)$ is the likelihood of the sample.
Then the posterior estimate of the reliability is

$$R(t) = \int_{-\infty}^{\infty} \int_{-\infty}^{\infty} \cdots \int_{-\infty}^{\infty} R(t|\lambda) D_1(\lambda_1|X_1) D_2(\lambda_2|X_2) \ldots D_k(\lambda_k|X_k) d\lambda_1 d\lambda_2 \ldots d\lambda_k .$$
(4)

In the case of a series system, the random variable X_0 is the
minimum $(X_1, X, \ldots, X_k)$. Then (1) may be written

$$R(t|\lambda) = \prod_{i=1}^{k} R_i(t|\lambda_i)$$
(5)

where $R_i(t|\lambda_i) = P_r\{X_i > t|\lambda_i\}$, and the prior and posterior estimates
of the reliability of the system become:

prior estimate: $R'(t) = \prod_{i=1}^{k} \int_{-\infty}^{\infty} R_i(t|\lambda_i) D'_i(\lambda_i) d\lambda_i = \prod_{i=1}^{k} E'[R_i(t|\lambda_i)]$
(6)

posterior estimate: $R(t) = \prod_{i=1}^{k} \int_{-\infty}^{\infty} R_i(t|\lambda_i) D_i(\lambda_i|X_i) d\lambda_i = \prod_{i=1}^{k} E[R_i(t|\lambda_i)]$.
(7)

The expectation on the r. h. s. of (6) is taken with respect to the
prior distribution (indicated by a prime) ; the expectation on the r. h. s.
of (7) is taken with respect to the posterior distribution.

Specializing to the situation where the distribution of the time to failure for the ith component is exponential with failure rate λ_i, we have

$$f_i(t, \lambda_i) = \lambda_i \exp - \lambda_i t$$

and

$$R_i(t \mid \lambda_i) = \exp - \lambda_i t .$$

Taking the prior distribution of λ_i to be gamma, i.e.

$$D'_i(\lambda_i) = \frac{z_i^r}{\Gamma(r)} \lambda_i^{r-1} e^{-\lambda_i z_i} \tag{8}$$

where z_i and r_i are parameters, the __prior__ estimate of the reliability (6) becomes

$$R'(t) = \prod_{i=1}^{k} E'[e^{-\lambda_i t}] = \prod_{i=1}^{k} \left[\frac{z_i}{z_i + t} \right]^{r_i} . \tag{9}$$

The posterior p.d.f. on λ_i may be written

$$D(\lambda_i \mid T_i) = \frac{(z_i + T_i)^{N_i}}{\Gamma(N_i)} \lambda_i^{N_i - 1} e^{-\lambda_i(z_i + T_i)} , \tag{10}$$

where $N_i = r_i + n_i$ and $T_i = \sum_{j=1}^{n_i} X_{ij}$ (the sum of the times-to-failure).

Hence the posterior estimate of the reliability (7) is

$$R(t) = \prod_{i=1}^{k} E[e^{-\lambda_i t}] = \prod_{i=1}^{k} \left[\frac{z_i + T_i}{z_i + T_i + t} \right]^{N_i} . \tag{11}$$

Note that as $n_i \to \infty$, $R(t) \to \prod_{i=1}^{k} e^{-\lambda_i t_i}$, independently of z_i and r_i; (here λ_i is the fixed parameter of the distribution sampled.) Thus, as the sample size increases, the effect of the prior distribution diminishes.

The main difference between our formulation of the reliability prediction problem and that of Dr. Rosenblatt's is that our model makes use of prior information. Many reliability estimation problems are based on small samples. We believe that ignoring the prior information obviates any useful estimate of system reliability.

One might wish to continue in this framework. Instead of computing confidence intervals, one could introduce utilities and attack the decision problem directly. The utilities would dictate the sampling plan and the final decision. (These remarks are in the spirit of the book by H. Raiffa and R. Schlaifer, Applied Statistical Decision Theory.)

The following written contribution was received after the seminar.

John K. Abraham. The confidence interval problem may be considered as related to the problem of interpreting R as an estimate. Due to assembly procedures and varying operating conditions, it cannot be expected that the artificially constructed devices will reflect perfectly the performance of the assembled systems. Therefore R as described in the paper might be interpreted as an estimate of some "true reliability" pertaining to the whole device. R might in fact follow a distribution of its own, in which case the true variance of the estimate of R would equal the variance of R plus the conditional variance of the estimate given R . In this case $\sigma^2(U)$ would pertain only to the second part, and hence underestimate the true variance of the estimate. This suggests that the resulting confidence interval might be too narrow, and that the probability of covering the true reliability would be less than intended. Ideally R would equal this number and the problem would thus not arise; however, this seems to be an unlikely possibility. From another point of view, the "true reliability" is a random variable, assumed to be drawn from a distribution having parameter (or parameters) related to R . Again the possibility exists that the probability of coverage would be less than intended.

Therefore, in applications of the present results, it seems that some investigation should be carried out concerning the nature of the estimate R ; in particular, how this number relates to a well-defined "true reliability."

Returning to the more immediate problem of estimating R , the following example provides some information about the estimation of Var(U) in the zero-one case:

For the series model, let $k = 5$, $R = \Pi p_i$, and $n_i = 100$ for all i , and suppose that the X_i (the number of successes observed) are 98, 100, 98, 99, and 97 respectively. It is not difficult to compute the variance of $U = \Pi(X_i/n_i)$, and to show that in this case, the unbiased estimate of the true variance of U (say $\hat{V}ar(U)$) turns out to be $.0^3703$. If one expands $U = f(\hat{p}_1, \ldots, \hat{p}_5)$ about the point $(p_1, \ldots, p_5)$ and uses the linear terms in an approximation to the variance, the unbiased estimate (which by the remarks in

Sections 3 and 4 equals $\hat{\sigma}^2(U)/100$) agrees with $\hat{Var}(U)$ to 6D ,
and the unbiased estimate of the variance of $\hat{R}_2 = U$, assuming that
it is binomially distributed with parameters $m = 100$ and R , is
$.0^3724$. The close agreement between $\hat{Var}(U)$ and $\hat{\sigma}^2(U)/100$
suggests that the expected values may be generally in close agreement, at least for series models. By expanding $Var(U)$, it can be
verified that as an upper bound,

$$Var(U) - \sigma^2(U)/m < (1-b)\left[\sum_i \binom{k}{i} b^i\right]$$

where $b = \max q_j/n_j$, $j = 1, \ldots, k$, and the sum is taken from 2 to
k . In the example, if $\max q_j$ is $.1$, the bound is $.0^5 9$, and even
if $\max q_j = 1/2$, the difference is still less than $.0^3 128$.
    However the difference between $[Var(U)]^{1/2}$ and $\sigma(U)/\sqrt{m}$
will be larger and because of the skewness of the distributions of
$\hat{\sigma}(U)$ and U , it may be that

$$[U - 1.645\hat{\sigma}(U)/\sqrt{m} , 1]$$

has an actual confidence coefficient appreciably different from $.95$,
and that a "widening" is necessary for at least some of the possible
parameter points. If one wishes to use a number greater than 1.645,
the problem of deciding which number to use arises for every model.
    It may be worthwhile that extensive computations eventually be
performed for specific cases (such as Πp_i , $\Pi(1-q_i^2)$, for say
$k = 2, 5$) comparing some of the proposed confidence intervals with
respect to some criterion or criteria.
    One criterion, for instance, might be as follows:
    Computations are made to determine the probabilities of the inter-
val covering R for various parameter points. The minimum probability
of covering R is sought over a given set (under the assumption that
an alpha-level interval for R is being used), through trial and error,
if necessary. Then for the given set this minimum probability of coverage constitutes the measure. The main advantage of this criterion
is that it provides a justification for statements made concerning the
minimum confidence coefficient actually attained for R . Secondary
criteria might be expected length, or ease of application, for example.
    Certainly computer results involving simple series and parallel
systems in the zero-one case for different confidence interval approaches would be useful in deciding for several problems which
procedure to use. Perhaps no one approach will give satisfactory
results for all zero-one systems, but at least some description of
the properties of the intervals would result.
    In section 2.2, it seems that variability is added by using R_1
rather than R_2 , as there is an immediate increase in variance with

randomization. This follows from the relationship

$$E[E(\hat{R}_1 - \hat{R}_2)^2 \mid X_1, \ldots, X_k] + \text{Var}(\hat{R}_2) = \text{Var}(\hat{R}_1) .$$

Dr. Rosenblatt replied at the seminar and later submitted the following in writing.

Joan Rosenblatt. I welcome the remarks by Dr. Steck on the need for extensive theoretical and numerical comparisons among various asymptotic and exact methods for constructing confidence intervals for system reliability. My paper does not sufficiently emphasize the fact that most of the approximate methods now available have not yet been shown to give useful results for small-to-moderate sample sizes. This is especially true of the approximate nonparametric method proposed in my paper. Some suggestions as to how a comparative study might be conducted have been contributed by Mr. Abraham.

Dr. Steck suggests that the structure function might be simplified through the use of the "minimal pathset" and "minimal cutset" notions to obtain upper and lower bounds. Another approach to simplification of the structure function is illustrated in detail by Abraham (1962). Abraham suggests that the structure function can often be factored into several independent factors which can be treated separately, the separate confidence limits (and confidence coefficients) being multiplied together finally. A combination of these two ideas might be useful in practice.

Mr. Abraham has contributed a useful warning about the dangers of interpreting estimates based on component data as estimates of system reliability. It cannot be too strongly emphasized that the usefulness of all methods is limited by the difficulty of establishing a useful representation $x_0 = f(x_1, \ldots, x_k)$ of system performance as a function of subsystem performances or characteristics.

Dr. Esary's remark has led to an amplification and clafification of the definition of the structure function $f(x_1, \ldots, x_k)$ in Section 4. The "standard form" of the structure function for the system used by Esary to illustrate his point would be

$$f(x_1, x_2, x_3) = x_1 x_2 x_3 + x_1 x_2 (1 - x_3) + x_1 (1 - x_2) x_3 .$$

The remarks by Dr. Zelen and Mr. Rotkin draw attention to important problems which arise when the populations of components are finite. The results of Connor and Wells (1962) can be applied to the study of the distribution of system reliability in the finite population case, when systems are assembled at random. Purposive selection of components would be more difficult to analyze mathematically.

Dr. Frishman considers a situation in which tests of a whole system have actually been performed, so that system reliability may

be estimated directly.   He then supposes further that the test results
provide data on subsystem performance and asks about the relation of
the direct estimate of R to an estimate composed of subsystem estimates.   The two estimates (and associated confidence limits) will
in general be different; the subsystem-data confidence interval for
R will often be shorter than the interval obtained directly from system
tests.   (The direct estimate is mathematically equivalent to $\hat{R}_1$ provided the mathematical model for the system is exact.)   It seems
clear, however, that estimates obtained directly from system tests
will usually be more trustworthy than estimates based on subsystem
data, since the latter require the assumption of some mathematical
model.

I thank Dr. Reinhardt and Dr. Zelen for contributing their interesting Bayesian calculation.   I will just add a remark amplifying
their opening paragraphs.   To obtain a point estimate of
$R = \exp \{-t \, \Sigma_i \theta_i^{-1}\}$, one could clearly substitute $\bar{x}_i$ for θ_i . A
theoretical justification for this, in terms of "optimum" properties, is
not obvious.

I am grateful to all of the participants in the discussion for their
stimulating comments and suggestions.   It is clear that a great deal
of work remains to be done on the problems studied in my paper, and
on the further problems raised during the discussion.

WILLIAM WOLMAN
Problems in system reliability analysis

1. SOME THOUGHTS ON RELIABILITY GROWTH

The following brief comments are oriented towards the field performance of complex systems. An example would be the flight of a missile or the orbiting of a satellite.

Failure in flight can be classified into types, either they are inherent failures or assignable cause failures. Each type of failure may or may not occur on a given flight. Hence, whether a failure occurs or not is a chance event. Inherent failures are failures whose assignable causes cannot be determined and are due to the interaction of the system and the environment at the particular time of flight. These failures cannot be eliminated by a design change. Assignable cause failures are those failures which can be eliminated by a design change or by some other means. This may involve such actions as part substitution, tightening up of quality control procedures, changing a tolerance, strengthening a material or a change in checkout procedure. The important distinction between this type of failure and an inherent failure is that a definite assignable cause has been established and that its future occurrence can be effectively prevented. It should be noted, however, that the occurrence of such assignable cause failures on a given flight is nevertheless due to chance—in that a combination of environment and other circumstances brings about the failure.

As the flight test program progesses, the assignable cause failures are eliminated by means of appropriate actions which are taken after each such flight failure. Inherent failures can, by definition, never be eliminated since they are an "inherent" characteristic of the system. One of the main purposes of the early flight test program is to expose the system to its true operating environment and induce those assignable cause failures which have not been eliminated in the ground test program. The elimination of assignable cause failures on successive flights provides a rationale for the reliability growth of a system during flight testing. It is, of course, assumed that no new failures are introduced in making the necessary design or procedural changes. These ideas may be summarized by the following schematic:

ELEMENTS OF RELIABILITY GROWTH

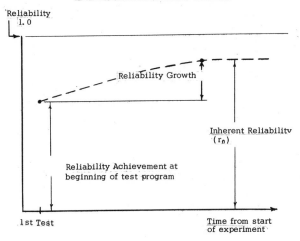

It shall be our purpose to express these ideas as an analytical model. Naturally, no model can ever fully explain the complex interrelationships and cause and effect aspects of a complex system such as the flight of a rocket launch vehicle with all its airborne and ground subsystems, components and parts.

2. RELIABILITY GROWTH MODEL

We shall consider the reliability growth of a system by using the following simple model. It is assumed that system failure may be due to either an inherent failure or a design weakness failure. Furthermore, inherent failures may occur with any trial, but a particular design weakness failure will not occur on a succeeding trial once it has occurred. The following definitions are made:

Type 1 failure = inherent system failure;

Type 2 failure = embryonic design weakness failure.

It is assumed that a system has k embryonic design weaknesses and

(1) on a given trial if a system failure occurs it is due to either a type 1 or type 2 failure;

(2) a type 1 failure can occur on any trial with probability q_0 ;

(3) each type 2 failure can occur only once and with probability q (i.e., they are eliminated between successive trials) ;

(4) the occurrence of type 1 and type 2 failures are independent; although, on a given trial of a system, failure is due to either one or the other.

A system can be defined as being in state "i" prior to a given trial if there have been "i" design weaknesses eliminated due to "i" type 2 failures on the previous trials. We indicate the state of the system by E_i . If prior to the trial the system was also in state E_i , then there are still $k-i$ type 2 failures remaining in the system. We next consider the conditional probability of the system S being in state E_{i+1} or E_i , depending on the outcome of a trial. It follows that

$$\Pr\{E_i | E_i\} = q_0 + r_0 p^{k-i} \qquad (1)$$

where

$$r_0 = 1 - q_0$$

$$p = 1 - q .$$

In (1) we are considering the probability of a system which is in state E_i and will not fail on a trial due to a type 2 failure, but may fail due to a type 1 failure. For the case where a trial results in a type 2 failure, we have

$$\Pr\{E_{i+1} | E_i\} = r_0(1 - p^{k-i}) \qquad (2)$$

or

$$\Pr\{E_i | E_{i-1}\} = r_0(1 - p^{k-i+1}) , \qquad (3)$$

for the conditional probability of the system being in state E_i or E_{i+1} with the occurrence of a type 2 failure.

Let us define

$$P_{ii}^{(1)} = q_0 + r_0 p^{k-i} \qquad i = 0, 1, \ldots, k ; \qquad (4)$$

$$P_{i-1, i}^{(1)} = r_0(1 - p^{k-i+1}) \qquad i = 1, 2, \ldots, k . \qquad (5)$$

Obviously, by (1), (2) and (3)

$$P_{i, i+1}^{(1)} + P_{ii}^{(1)} = 1$$

since

$$P_{i, i+1}^{(1)} = r_0(1 - p^{k-i}) = r_0 - r_0 p^{k-i} = 1 - q_0 - r_0 p^{k-i}$$

$$= 1 - (q_0 + r_0 p^{k-i})$$

$$= 1 - P_{ii}^{(1)} .$$

Since the probability of the system being in state E_i depends only on the state of the system on the previous trial and not on any other previous trials, it is natural to consider the stochastic process as a Markov chain with transition probabilities given by (4) and (5). We next define the transition matrix of order $k+1$ by

$$P = \begin{bmatrix} P_{00}^{(1)} P_{01}^{(1)} & \cdots & P_{0k}^{(1)} \\ P_{10}^{(1)} P_{11}^{(1)} & \cdots & P_{1k}^{(1)} \\ \vdots & \ddots & \vdots \\ P_{k0}^{(1)} P_{k1}^{(1)} & \cdots & P_{kk}^{(1)} \end{bmatrix}$$

where $P_{ii}^{(1)}$, $P_{i,\,i+1}^{(1)}$ are defined by (4) and (5), and $P_{ij}^{(1)} = 0$, otherwise.

It is of interest to note that

$$P_{kk}^{(1)} = q_0 + r_0 = 1 . \tag{6}$$

Equation (6) represents the probability of remaining in state E_k if one has reached it on any previous trial; therefore E_k is an absorption state. The elements of the matrix P represent the respective probabilities for reaching the state E_i or E_{i+1} from state E_i in a single trial. If we consider the elements of P^n, designated by $P_{ij}^{(n)}$, we obtain the n-th passage transition probabilities. They represent the probabilities of going from state E_i to state E_j in n trials. Of particular interest are the elements

$$P_{0i}^{(n)} = \Pr\{E_i \text{ after } n \text{ trials}\} , \qquad i \le n \text{ and } i = 0, 1, \ldots, k, \tag{7}$$

where

$$\sum_{i=0}^{k} P_{0i}^{(n)} = 1 ,$$

since they represent the probability of eliminating i type 2 failures in n trials. Especially, the term

$$P_{0k}^{(n)} = \Pr\{E_k \text{ in } n \text{ trials}\}$$

is important because it is the probability of having eliminated all type 2 failures in n trials.

We shall now be concerned with the problem of finding P^n. It is noted that P is a triangular matrix with zeros for all elements below the principal diagonal.

Since the product of triangular matrices is also triangular, with zeros below the principal diagonal it follows that P^n is triangular. The characteristic roots of P are the solution of the following question:

$$|P - \lambda I| = 0 \ . \tag{8}$$

Since P is triangular it follows that

$$(q_0 + r_0 p^k - \lambda)(q_0 + r_0 p^{k-1} - \lambda) \ldots (1 - \lambda) = 0 \ ,$$

and we obtain

$$\lambda_i = q_0 + r_0 p^{k-i} \ , \quad i = 0, 1, \ldots, k \tag{9}$$

for the $k+1$ distinct characteristic roots. We define the characteristic row vectors $x_0, x_1, \ldots, x_k$ of $k+1$ elements each by

$$x_i(P - \lambda_i I) = 0 \ . \tag{10}$$

We next define the matrix X which consists of the row vectors x_i, $i = 0, 1, \ldots, k$, and also

$$\Lambda = \begin{bmatrix} \lambda_0 & & & & \\ & \lambda_1 & & 0 & \\ & & \cdot & & \\ 0 & & & \cdot & \\ & & & & \lambda_k \end{bmatrix}$$

It follows from (10) that

$$x_i P' = \lambda_i x_i$$

and

$$XP' = \Lambda X \ . \tag{11}$$

Rao in [1] shows that X has an inverse and hence

$$P' = X^{-1} \Lambda X \ . \tag{12}$$

We next define

$$X' = Y^{-1}$$

and hence

$$P = X' \Lambda X'^{-1}$$
$$= Y^{-1} \Lambda Y \ .$$

We obtain for $P \cdot P$

$$P^2 = Y^{-1} \Lambda Y Y^{-1} \Lambda Y$$

$$= Y^{-1} \Lambda^2 Y$$

and

$$P^n = Y^{-1} \Lambda^n Y . \tag{13}$$

Since the elements of Λ are defined by (9), it is only necessary to find the matrix of characteristic vectors. Feller in [2] gives an alternative procedure for finding the elements of P^n, however, in view of the fact that the characteristic roots of P can be immediately obtained, the method outlined above is considered preferable. The basic model and the Markov chain approach to this problem first came to my attention through reference [3].

Example for case $k = 2$

$$X = \begin{bmatrix} 1 & 0 & 0 \\ \left(\dfrac{1-\lambda_0}{\lambda_1 - \lambda_0}\right) & 1 & 0 \\ 1 & 1 & 1 \end{bmatrix}$$

$$\lambda_i = q_0 + r_0 p^{k-i} , \quad i = 0, 1, 2 .$$

The reliability after the n-th trial can then be defined by

$$R(n) = \sum_{i=0}^{k} r_0 p^{k-i} \cdot P_{0i}^{(n)} .$$

It can be easily shown that

$$\lim_{n \to \infty} P_{0i}^{(n)} = 0 \quad \text{for } i = 0, 1, \ldots, k-1$$

$$= 1 \quad \text{for } i = k$$

and hence

$$\lim_{n \to \infty} R(n) = r_0 .$$

The simple model considered can be extended in the following manner:

1. Let each type 2 failure occur with unequal probability, say q_i, $i = 1, \ldots, k$.

2. Assume that a type 2 failure is not eliminated after a single occurrence. In this case we assume that the i-th type 2 failure is eliminated after it has occurred,

say α_i times $\alpha_i = 1, \ldots, s$.

3. Assume that some of the type 2 failure modes are redundant. Namely, the system will only fail if failure occurs for both the primary and the redundant element.

4. Consider the reliability growth of say a two-stage launch vehicle where the second stage does not have an opportunity to function unless the first stage has functioned successfully.

5. Assume that the probability of occurrence of the i-th failure mode is not only dependent on the item involved but also depends on the trial, namely, $q_i = q_i(n)$, where n represents the n-th trial.

The modifications of the model considered above represent only some of the extensions which may be made to make the model more realistic.

3. RELATIONSHIP BETWEEN PROBABILITY OF FAILURE MODES AND OCCURRENCE OF SYSTEM FAILURE

We consider a system which consists of 2 component types, A and B, such that system failure can be due to either a type A failure or a type B failure. It is convenient to display the difference between system failure due to a component and the failure of a component by the following Venn diagram, where the symbols for the different sets represent the associated probabilities which are defined in the following remarks.

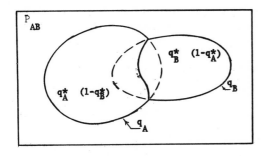
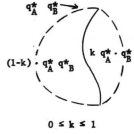

We define

$$P_A^* = P_r \{\text{failure type } A \text{ will } \underline{\text{not}} \text{ occur}\}$$
$$P_B^* = P_r \{\text{failure type } B \text{ will } \underline{\text{not}} \text{ occur}\}$$
$$q_A^* = 1 - p_A^*$$
$$q_B^* = 1 - p_B^*$$.

Assume that the occurrence of the failure types are independent. Hence

$$\text{Pr}\{\text{occurrence of failure types   A and B}\} = q_A^* \cdot q_B^*$$

However, on a given system trial (e.g. a flight test) if failure mode A occurs, then mode B has no longer the opportunity to occur, and similarly if mode B occurs, A cannot occur. Let us assume a mission time from 0 to t and let

$q_A = \text{Pr}\{A \text{ fails at } t^*, B \underline{\text{not}} \text{ failed at } t^*, B \text{ may or may not fail between}$ t^* and $t\}$

where,
$$0 < t^* < t \ ;$$
hence
$$q_A = \text{Pr}\{A \text{ fails before B}\} \ .$$

Also, let
$$P_{AB} = \text{Pr}\{\text{neither failure types A or B occur}\}.$$

Since on a given system trial we can observe the failure of A or B or success, we have

$$P_{AB} + q_A + q_B = 1 \ . \tag{14}$$

However, in terms of the individual independent failures modes

$$(1 - q_A^*)(1 - q_B^*) = P_{AB} \ . \tag{15}$$

Using equations (14) and (15) we obtain the equation

$$q_A^* + q_B^* - q_A^* q_B^* = q_A + q_B \ . \tag{16}$$

In order to find the relationship between q* and q , it is necessary to make assumptions regarding the relative frequency of occurrence of failure for types A and B during 0 to t . We may write for the probability of failure of A $\underline{\text{and}}$ B , which is an event which cannot be observed in the system considered,

$\text{Pr}\{\text{occurrence of failure of A and B}\}$

$= \text{Pr}\{B \text{ fails before A fails}\} + \text{Pr}\{A \text{ fails before B fails}\}$

$= q_A^* q_B^*$

We write the identity

$$q_A^* q_B^* \equiv k \, q_A^* q_B^* + (1-k) q_A^* q_B^* \ , \qquad 0 \leq k \leq 1 \ , \tag{17}$$

where we define

$$k = \Pr\{B \text{ fails before A fails} \mid A \text{ and } B \text{ fail}\}$$
$$1 - k = \Pr\{A \text{ fails before B fails} \mid A \text{ and } B \text{ fail}\}$$

where,

$$q_A^* q_B^* = \Pr\{A \text{ and } B \text{ fail}\} .$$

We express the component failure probability q_A^* as

$$q_A^* = q_A + \Pr\{B \text{ fails before A fails}\} \tag{18}$$

$$q_A^* = q_A + k\, q_A^* q_B^* \tag{19}$$

and similarly

$$q_B^* = q_B + (1-k)\, q_A^* q_B^* . \tag{20}$$

Adding (19) and (20) we obtain equation (16), namely

$$q_A^* + q_B^* - q_A^* q_B^* = q_A + q_B .$$

In (18) the two probabilities on the r.h.s. are associated with two mutually exclusive outcomes for a given system trial since q_A is the probability that A fails first regardless of B and the second that A fails <u>after</u> B fails. For the case of a uniform failure density over the interval from 0 to t we have

$$\Pr\{A \text{ fails before B}\} = \Pr\{A \text{ fails 1st}\} = q_A = q_A^*(1-q_B^*) + \frac{q_A^* q_B^*}{2} \tag{21}$$

and

$$\Pr\{B \text{ fails before A}\} = \Pr\{B \text{ fails 1st}\} = q_B = q_B^*(1-q_A^*) + \frac{q_A^* q_B^*}{2} . \tag{22}$$

We show this as follows. By definition we have that

Pr{A fails before B fails}

$$= \Pr\{A \text{ fails before B fails} \mid A \text{ and } B \text{ fail}\} \Pr\{A \text{ and } B \text{ fail}\} .$$

However, we showed that

$$\Pr\{A \text{ and } B \text{ fail}\} = q_A^* \cdot q_B^* .$$

We must therefore show that

$$\Pr\{A \text{ fails before B fails} \mid A \text{ and } B \text{ fail}\} = \tfrac{1}{2}, \tag{23}$$

where we assume that the time of failure of A and B is uniform over the interval from 0 to t. We therefore have the following density function (conditional) for A and B type failures

$$f(t_A) = \frac{1}{t}, \quad 0 \le t_A \le t \tag{24}$$

$$= 0 \quad \text{otherwise}$$

and similarly for $f(t_B)$. Hence, the joint (conditional) density is

$$f(t_A, t_B) = f(t_A) \cdot f(t_B) = \frac{1}{t^2}, \quad 0 \le t_A, t_B \le t. \tag{25}$$

And, if we want the conditional probability of A failing before B failing, we have

$$\int_0^t \int_{t_A}^t \frac{1}{t^2} \, dt_B dt_A \tag{26}$$

$$= \frac{1}{t^2} \int_0^t (t - t_A) \, dt_A$$

$$= \frac{1}{2}.$$

This result is obvious since we are concerned with the conditional probability of A failing before B failing where both are assumed to be uniformly distributed over $(0, t)$. The result of (26) holds more general, namely for all cases where the failure distribution for types A and B is identical.

If the time to failure is exponential, then the probability of A failing before B failing can be found in a similar manner with the following density replacing (25), namely

$$f(t_A, t_B) = \frac{\lambda_A \lambda_B e^{-\lambda_A t_A - \lambda_B t_B}}{(1 - e^{-\lambda_A t})(1 - e^{-\lambda_B t})}, \quad 0 \le t_A, t_B \le t \tag{27}$$

where λ_A and λ_B are the parameters of the exponential distribution. It follows that

$$\Pr\{A \text{ fails before B fails} \mid A \text{ and } B \text{ fail before } t\} \tag{28}$$

$$= \int_0^t \int_{t_A}^t f(t_A, t_B) \, dt_B dt_A$$

where $f(t_A, t_B)$ is given by (27), and this reduces to

$$\frac{1}{(1-e^{-\lambda_A t})(1-e^{-\lambda_B t})} \left[\frac{\lambda_A}{\lambda_A + \lambda_B} + \frac{\lambda_B}{\lambda_A + \lambda_B} e^{-(\lambda_A+\lambda_B)t} - e^{-\lambda_B t} \right]$$

$$\tag{29}$$

Since

$$\lim_{t \to \infty} e^{-\lambda t} = 0 , \quad \text{for } \lambda > 0$$

expression (29) reduces to

$$\frac{\lambda_A}{\lambda_A + \lambda_B} \tag{30}$$

as $t \to \infty$. This result can then be considered as a "steady state" solution for the conditional probability that A fails before B fails.

It can also be shown that given any two density functions f_A and f_B and the corresponding cumulative distributions functions F_A and F_B that

$$\Pr \{ A \text{ fails before B fails} \mid A \text{ and B fail before } t \}$$

$$= 1 - \int_0^t \frac{f_A(\chi) F_B(\chi)}{F_A(t) F_B(t)} d\chi .$$

Extending these ideas to more than two failure modes is straightforward although computationally tedious in actual applications.

EXAMPLES

Let us assume a uniform distribution of failure over the interval 0 to t.

1. Suppose we assume the following system failure rates and wish to obtain the component failure rates:

$$q_A = .19$$

$$q_B = .09$$

Then,

$$P_{AB} = 1 - q_A - q_B = .72$$

$$= (1 - q_A^*)(1 - q_B^*) .$$

Solving equations (21) and (22)

$$q_A^* = \frac{(q_A - q_B + 2) - [(q_A - q_B + 2)^2 - 8q_A]^{\frac{1}{2}}}{2}$$

$$q_A^* = \tfrac{1}{2}(2.10 - 1.70)$$

$$q_A^* = .20 .$$

Also, from (16),

$$q_B^* = \frac{q_A + q_B - q_A^*}{1 - q_A^*} = .10$$

We check the results by finding that

$$P_{AB} = (1 - q_A^*)(1 - q_B^*) = (.80)(.90) = .72$$

2. If $q_A = q_B = q$, $0 \le q \le .50$

then,

$$q^* = 1 - \sqrt{1 - 2q}$$

and for the case where $q = .5$, $q^* = 1$. In this case, the proba-bility of each component failing is one; however, each component in the system is only observed to fail in half of all system trials. This extreme example shows that failure rates, based on system tests, should not be used without fully realizing that they may seriously underestimate component failure rates.

In the remarks above, I have not considered the important prob-lem of how to estimate q_A^* and q_B^* given estimates of q_A and q_B . However, the expression for q_A^* in example (1) above, suggests the replacing of q_A and q_B with the observed percentage of failure for each component on the system tests.

REFERENCES

(1) Rao, C.R.: Advanced Statistical Methods in Biometric Research, Wiley and Sons, Inc., New York, 1952, 1-31.

(2) Feller, W.: An Introduction to Probability Theory and Its Appli-cations, vol. I, Second ed., John Wiley and Sons, Inc., New York, 1957, Chap. XVI.

(3) Internal Memo from R. Herrmann to B. Bertrando (General Electric Technical Military Planning Operation) dtd 9/7/61, subj: Relia-bility Growth in a System Containing Both a Known Inherent Re-liability and a Given Number of Removable Defects, each having the same Occurrence Rate.

DISCUSSION OF THE PAPER BY DR. WOLMAN

W. S. Connor. Because time is short for those who wish to make early travel connections, I shall make only a few comments. First of all, I would like to express my personal appreciation to Dr. Zelen and the Mathematics Research Center for this excellent seminar which we have had the pleasure of attending. I believe that it will contribute significantly to the advance of the theory and practice of probabilistic and statistical methodology in reliability. Secondly, I wish to congratulate Dr. Wolman on the interesting paper which he has just presented.

Dr. Wolman has brought to our attention two reliability problems which are of wide interest and deserve study beyond the investigation which he himself has conducted and has described to us. The first problem is concerned with the improvement of the reliability of a system by the sequential correction of defects which are revealed by a succession of flight tests. The second problem is concerned with the determination of the reliabilities of components from systems tests which identify only the initial component which fails, and yield no observable information about the subsequent failure of other components. I would like to make a few brief remarks about Dr. Wolman's treatment of each of these problems.

With respect to the first problem, it appears that there are two assumptions implied by the formulae which I would like to stress. The first assumption is that the occurrence of a Type 1 failure, i.e., a failure which is inherent and uncorrectable, precludes any information about whether or not a Type 2 failure has occurred. The second assumption is that not more than one of the k Type 2 failures, i.e., failures which are due to faulty design and can be corrected, is detectable and corrected by a single flight.

Working under these assumptions, a formula has been developed for calculating the probability of finding and correcting $i \leq k$ Type 2 causes of failure in $n \geq i$ trials. Also the reliability of the system after the $n\underline{th}$ trial has been calculated.

By excluding those flights which are successful and considering only those flights in which Type 1 or Type 2 failures occur, it is easy to calculate reliability growth relative to the number of failures experienced. The probability of m-i Type 1 failures occurring in m trials (where all m trials result in failure) is given by the binomial probability function

$$(^m_{m-i}) q_0^{m-i} (1 - q_0)^m .$$

Because the remaining trials produce Type 2 failures, the above probability is $P^{(m)}_{0i}$, the probability of eliminating i Type 2 causes of failure in m trials which result in failure.

Of course, neglecting successful flights does not enable one to calculate the reliability after n trials or the number of trials required to achieve a specified reliability. The latter problem can be treated in the following way. The quantity

$$(P_{ii}^{(1)})^{n_i}(1 - P_{ii}^{(1)})$$

is the probability that $(n_i + 1)$ trials will be needed in order to pass from state E_i to state E_{i+1}. It is recognized to be a point density for the geometric distribution. The sum

$$\sum_{i=1}^{\infty} n_i (P_{ii}^{(1)})^{n_i - 1}(1 - P_{ii}^{(1)}) = (1 - P_{ii}^{(1)})^{-1}$$

is the average number of trials required to pass from state E_i to state E_{i+1}. Accordingly,

$$\sum_{i=0}^{j-1} (1 - P_{ii}^{(1)})^{-1}, \qquad j \le k$$

is the average number of trials required to reach state j.

A more general problem than the one discussed by Dr. Wolman would result from relaxing the second assumption and allowing more than one Type 2 failure to be discovered and corrected by a single test flight. It would seem that the solution of this problem would find useful applications. A still more general model would permit the discovery of more than one cause of Type 1 and Type 2 failures on a single trial.

With respect to the second problem, I agree with the author that it would be useful to consider a system with more than two modes of failure. In addition, other distributions of failure over time could be studied.

The paper does not consider the statistical estimation of probabilities of failure, with the exception of a remark at the end about the estimation of q_A and q_B. I believe that substantial attention should be given to the discovery of desirable point and interval estimators of unknown probabilities of the kind defined in this paper.

In conclusion, I would again like to express my personal thanks to Dr. Wolman for this very stimulating paper.

George Weiss. An explicit solution can be given for Wolman's model without the matrix calculations. Let $\pi_i(n)$ denote the probability that i design failures have been eliminated after n trials have been run. Then, using Wolman's notation

$$\pi_0(n) = [q_0 + r_0 p^k]^n \; . \tag{1}$$

We can derive a recurrence relation for the $\pi_i(n)$ of the form

$$\pi_i(n+1) = a_i \pi_i(n) + b_i \pi_{i-1}(n) \tag{2}$$

where

$$a_i = q_0 + r_0 p^{k-i}$$
$$b_i = r_0(1 - p^{k-i+1}) \; . \tag{3}$$

Equation (2) is derived by noting that if i embryonic failures have been eliminated by $n+1$ trials, then after n trials there were either i embryonic failures and non occurred or was detected in the remaining trial, or $i-1$ failures were detected in n trials, and a further one was detected on the $n + 1$'st trial. The values in Eq. (3) are derived from Wolman's paper. The system reliability after n trials is

$$R(n) = \sum_{i=0}^{k} r_0 p^{k-i} \pi_i(n) \; . \tag{4}$$

Equation (2) can be solved by introducing the generating function

$$P_i(s) = \sum_{i=0}^{\infty} \pi_i(n) s^n \tag{5}$$

together with the initial value

$$P_0(s) = \frac{1}{1 - (q_0 + r_0 p^k) s} = \frac{1}{1 - a_0 s} \; . \tag{6}$$

It is then easily verified that the $P_i(s)$ satisfy the recurrence relation

$$P_i(s) = a_i s P_i(s) + b_i P_{i-1}(s) \tag{7}$$

with the solution

$$P_i(s) = \frac{b_i P_{i-1}(s)}{1 - a_i s} = \frac{b_1 b_2 \dots b_i}{(1 - a_0 s)(1 - a_1 s) \dots (1 - a_i s)} \; . \tag{8}$$

In this expression for $P_i(s)$ we can expand by partial fractions yielding

$$P_i(s) = b_1 b_2 \ldots b_i \sum_{m=0}^{i}{}' \frac{a_m^i}{(a_m - a_0)(a_m - a_1) \ldots (a_m - a_i)} \frac{1}{(1 - a_m s)}$$

(9)

where the prime indicates that the term with a zero denominator is to be omitted. With this result we find the expression for $\pi_i(b)$:

$$\pi_i(n) = b_1 b_2 \ldots b_i \sum_{m=0}^{i}{}' \frac{a_m^{i+n}}{(a_m - a_0)(a_m - a_1) \ldots (a_m - a_i)}$$

(10)

$$= (1 - p^k)(1 - p^{k-1}) \ldots (1 - p^{k-i}) \sum_{m=0}^{i}{}' \frac{[q_0 + r_0 p^{k-m}]^{i+n} p^{i(m-n)}}{(1 - p^m)(1 - p^{m-1}) \ldots (1 - p^{m-i})} .$$

The reliability after n trials is now found by substituting this expression into Eq. (4). A similar analysis is easily carried out when the probabilities for embryonic failures differ from each other.

Dr. Flehinger has suggested that the present method of solution might also be used to discuss the case where embryonic defects are not necessarily discovered when they occur. If we assume that an embryonic failure is only repaired with probability θ then the present model applies, except that the parameters a_i and b_i are now given by

$$a_i = q_0 + r_0[p^{k-i} + (1-\theta) iqp^{k-i-1}]$$

$$b_i = \theta r_0(1 - p^{k-i+1}) .$$

(11)

W.J. Corcoran. 1. We in the Special Projects Office have also been interested in this question of reliability growth. The model we have been working with is multinomial where initial reliability p_0 is given by $p_0 = 1 - (q_1 + q_2 + \ldots + q_k)$ with $\Sigma q_i \leq 1$. The $\{q_i\}$ are not necessarily equal so the gain in reliability after a failure, and elimination of the guilty failure mode, is a matter of chance. Hence p_r, the reliability after r failures, is stochastic. On simulation tests with a variety of choices for the $\{q_i\}$ we have found a straight-line relationship on semi-log graph paper between p_r and r (i.e., $\log p_r = a + br$).

2. I find it hard to visualize a model fitting the assumptions in Dr. Wolman's paper. The development in the paper implies that the reliability p_i after i failures of Type II is given by $p_i = (1-q_0)(1-q)^{k-}$ This is characteristic of a test which proceeds sequentially. If there

is independence for probability of occurrence of failure modes, this is consistent with a test that goes to completion whether or not a failure occurs, but it is inconsistent with the statement that only one failure may occur in a test. If we accept that only one failure mode may occur this is consistent with a test which stops at the instant of failure, but it is inconsistent with the statement of independence since, e.g., a high probability of failure early in the sequence means a low probability late in the sequence. It is hard to see how both assumptions can be satisfied at the same time in this sequential model. They are of course exactly satisfied in a multinomial model.

3. Extending my remarks under #1 above, we found for the general multinomial model that

$$\bar{N}_{ij} \sim \left(\frac{1}{1-p_j} - \frac{1}{1-p_i}\right)$$

where $\bar{N}_{ij}$ is the average number of tests to achieve a reliability p_j starting from p_i. This can be written in the form $\frac{1}{1-p_i}\left(\frac{1-p_i}{1-p_j} - 1\right)$ which brings out the strong dependence of $\bar{N}_{ij}$ on the starting reliability for a given fractional reduction in "unreliability."

Nathan Mantel. Under Wolman's Model, I think his results can be obtained directly from considering the multinomial distribution without recourse to transition matrices. Suppose, conceptually, one did not make corrections following the appearance and detection of an embryonic failure. Then following n trials the terms of the multinomial would give the joint probability that failures of type j occurred f_j times, $j = 1, \ldots, k$, that inherent failures occurred f_0 times, and that success occurred f_{k+1} times. (Failures of type j, $j = 1, \ldots, k$, occurring beyond the first can be interpreted as successes where corrections are being made.) The probability that failure j will occur and be detected in n trials equals the sum of the multinomial terms for which $f_j \geq 1$. The probability that exactly i types of failure will have occurred and been detected in n trials equals the sum of the multinomial terms for which the number of f_j's ≥ 1, $j = 1, \ldots, k$, equals i. It becomes easy also to determine the expected improvement in reliability by trial n. This is simply the sum of probabilities for each of the embryonic failures to have occurred at least once and is obtained readily considering simple binomials. Where i types of embryonic failure have already occurred at least once, the expected number of trials to occurrence of still another type of embryonic failure is $1/(k-i)q$, in the case of uniform probabilities for the various types of embryonic failure.

With the multinomial approach two complicating factors mentioned by Wolman are readily handled. These are: (1) unequal probabilities of embryonic failure, and (2) requirement that an embryonic failure occur several times before it can be detected.

Weinstein. Multiple "assignable" failures can surely occur on the same flight vehicle without necessarily causing abort of the mission. For example, poor control of fuel metering would not necessarily cause abort and would permit the flight to exhibit presence of other types of "assignable" failures.

[Dr. Wolman responded that modes which will not cause mission failure are not considered in the model discussed.]

M. Zelen. 1. Assuming this model of reliability growth is modified to take into account many of the features which were left out, how, and for what purpose, would one use the model?

Wolman. One use would be to estimate the minimum number of flights needed to achieve a target level of reliability.

Zelen. 2. Also, I think your development is only one part of the general framework. One of the important problems is to decide when one should stop ground testing and go into flight testing. One only does this when further ground testing does not reveal serious defects and feels that nothing major can be gained without going into flight tests. Deciding when to go into flight testing from ground testing seems to me to be a critical problem. Here is where a reliability growth model is needed.

Wolman. This would certainly be another important use.

Dr. Wolman replied at the seminar and later submitted the following in writing:

W. Wolman. With regard to Capt. Corcoran's comment, the important point is to distinguish between the probability of failure due to a particular mode (or component) and the probability of a system failure due to this component. This question is discussed in considerable detail in the second part of my paper. In the part of my paper dealing with growth curves, I am considering independent failure modes, whereas Capt. Corcoran is referring to system failure due to components—and considers these events mutually exclusive. The two points of view are not inconsistent but result in a different formulation and estimation procedure of the parameters.

Dr. Weiss' use of the recurrence equation and its solution is certainly applicable and interesting. Concerning Mr. Mantel's contribution, without additional details, I don't see how he solves the problem.